EARTH RESOURCES, ENERGY, AND THE ENVIRONMENT

DOUGLAS G. BROOKINS
University of New Mexico

WITHDRAWN

CHARLES E. MERRILL PUBLISHING COMPANY
A BELL & HOWELL COMPANY
Columbus   Toronto   London   Sydney

Published by Charles E. Merrill Publishing Co.
A Bell & Howell Company
Columbus, Ohio 43216

This book was set in Optima.
Text Designer: Ann Mirels
Production Coordination: Jo Ellen Gohr
Cover Design Coordination: Will Chenoweth
Cover photograph by Don Green, courtesy of Kennecott
Copper Corporation.

Library of Congress Catalog Card Number: 80–82786
International Standard Book Number: 0–675–08113–0
Printed in the United States of America
1 2 3 4 5 6 7 8 9 10—85 84 83 82 81

At no time in our history has the public been more aware of problems dealing with energy. Current supplies and prices of fuels are uncertain, and the public is concerned about future energy supplies and demand. An optimistic view is that a solution to the energy situation will be found in the near future; the United States' choices are nuclear or coal power plants, and the merits of each must be weighed carefully.

Most individuals, however, are not aware of our minerals situation. Many commodities, exclusive of fuels, are already in short supply and may be virtually exhausted early in the twenty-first century. Substitutes for many of these commodities, especially some metals, will certainly be available; yet for many others no such substitutes exist. More efficient ways of handling potash, sulfur, and phosphorus—elements critical to agriculture— must be found. Only nitrogen, which is extracted from the atmosphere, is in adequate supply. Population growth in the next century and more efficient ways of recovering (and recycling) water will influence consumption of these elements. Indeed, population growth and the degree of industrialization throughout the world will ultimately control consumption of all natural resources and require more efficient energy and resource conservation measures.

The impact on the environment of any method of excavation, whether for highway construction or for mining activities, must be carefully evaluated. Only now is the overall geochemistry of the environment and the effect of disturbing the earth's surface by excavation being understood. In addition, the problem of wastes, including non-radioactive chemical wastes, radioactive wastes, and waste rock and soil from excavations, and the correlation of various aspects of health and disease with the geochemistry of rocks and soils are being considered.

This text explores, in an elementary fashion, our diminishing earth resources, the choice of energy alternatives, and the resulting environmental impact. Although a familiarity with geology is helpful, the main themes of the text can be understood with occasional references to any introductory geology text.

Many individuals have assisted me in preparing and compiling data for this book. Professors Wolfgang Elston and Ronald Knief of the University of New Mexico allowed me to use some of their unpublished materials. Paul E. Myers of the University of Wisconsin–Eau Claire and William Blackburn of the University of Kentucky re-

Preface

viewed the manuscript, and many of their suggestions were incorporated into the text. Students from beginning classes to the highest graduate levels have offered constructive advice on various subjects. The U.S. Geological Survey, the U.S. Bureau of Mines, and many other U.S. agencies have provided current, factual information. Finally, I wish to thank the staff of the Charles E. Merrill Publishing Company for their assistance.

Contents

Introduction

Earth resources, energy, and *environment*— these are three terms to which we are exposed in our everyday life. Sometimes we fully understand statements using these terms; at other times we are only vaguely familiar with the subject.

This book introduces the student to some aspects of earth resources and energy, with appropriate comments intertwined regarding the environment. It is not intended to be a text for economic geology, nor an exhaustive look at energy or the environment. Additional readings are listed at the end of the book.

Any resource from any part of the animal, vegetable, or mineral kingdoms on the earth is an earth resource. Yet in this book we are concerned with only those commodities which are, by convention, discussed together as *mineral resources*. It is to these very resources that we owe our existence.

Renewable and Nonrenewable Resources

Mineral resources may be classified as *renewable* or *nonrenewable*. A renewable resource, after use, will eventually be available again. For some resources, such as water, the lag time between initial use and renewal may be so long that for practical purposes the resource becomes nonrenewable. Nonrenewable resources include those commodities that, once used, are never again available. For example, burning fossil fuels, splitting atoms, and alloying metals removes these substances from use by future generations.

A *reserve* is that part of a resource for which we have very precise quality

INTRODUCTION

and quantity information (for example, at least a 90 percent probability that a certain amount of rock will yield a specific tonnage of metal). For mineral commodities, such information is best obtained by drilling, assaying the drill core or cuttings, and combining the drill information with geologic input. When the limits of an ore-bearing unit of rock are known with varying degrees of confidence, we refer to the corresponding reserves contained therein as *proved, probable,* or *possible* (i.e., ranging from a very high level of confidence to a relatively uncertain degree of confidence, but still based on some firm criteria).

As shown in Figures 1–1 and 1–2, we distinguish *reserves* from *resources.* Some resources will be added to, or subtracted from, reserves as economic conditions change. Other resources are classified as hypothetical (or undiscovered). The assumption is that additions to reserves are more likely from known mining areas and less likely from similar areas of little or no mineral exploitation. In Figure 1–1 the line A–B can fluctuate up or down. It merely serves to separate low-grade *proven–probable–possible* ore from higher grade ore. Should the price of the material increase, then the line A–B will move down. For hypothetical resources two categories can be defined: undiscovered ore from known areas of ore occurrence, and undiscovered ore from areas where some geologic criteria indicate ore favorability but from which no ore deposits are known. Only when sufficient drilling or other techniques have been employed to indicate the presence of some ore can hypothetical ore be properly classified as a reserve.

In Figure 1–2, area **A** shows many drill holes (the vertical lines) from which the rock has been assayed. In area **B** there are fewer drill holes but the grade (*tenor*) of the ore and the thickness of the ore horizon

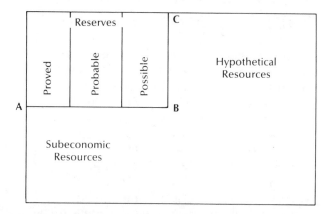

FIGURE 1–1 Distinguishing between reserves and resources. *Reserves* are economically recoverable materials from identified deposits, as distinguished from *resources* of the same material from identified but subeconomic or hypothetical deposits.

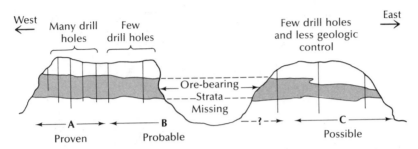

FIGURE 1–2 Classification of reserves. This cross section of ore-bearing strata (from west to east) illustrates proven-probable-possible ore reserves.

are about the same as for area **A**. Further east the ore horizon thins and the tenor of the ore drops, too. These factors, coupled with lack of drill holes, would dictate that the ore reserves be classified as *possible*. In addition, assuming that the tenor of the ore did not decrease as shown but the thickness of the unit did decrease, then the ore classified as *possible* might be more properly classified as *subeconomic*—that is, too much barren rock would have to be removed to recover the ore profitably.

Formation of Ores

Crustal abundance and the way in which chemical elements are incorporated into minerals are the controlling factors for ore formation. In addition to a relatively high concentration of an element in the rock, atoms of the element must be bonded to other atoms in such a way that extraction can be profitable. Aluminum is a classic example. Although it is the third most abundant metal (by weight) in the earth's crust, only certain minerals (e.g., gibbsite, an aluminum hydroxide abundant in bauxite deposits) can be treated for profitable removal of aluminum. The aluminum in the very common rock-forming minerals such as the feldspars and micas is so tightly bonded that it cannot be profitably extracted. (Refer to Appendix 1, which lists the elements and their symbols and other useful information, and Appendix 2, which displays the elements in the periodic table as groups with similar chemical characteristics.) Figure 1–3 illustrates how different elements must be present in specific concentrations before they can be properly classified as reserves.

Figure 1–3 also demonstrates that we can arrive at tonnages of minable elements by multiplying their crustal abundance by a factor ranging between one and ten billion. Despite obvious uncertainties such as degree of exploration and other factors, this method has worked well

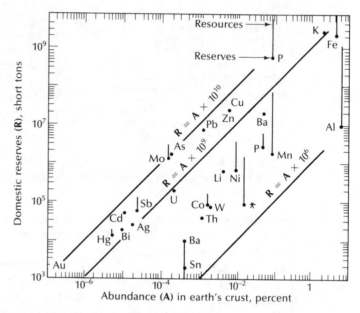

FIGURE 1–3 Domestic reserves compared to crustal abundance of elements. In general, the reserves (**R**) are equal to the abundance (**A**) times a factor varying from one million (10^6) to one billion (10^9), as illustrated by the 45° slopes. The vertical bars for different elements connect ore minable now (shown by dots) to deposits where it is hoped that technological breakthroughs will allow the lower grade sub-ore to be economically mined in the future. (From V. E. McKelvey, U.S. Geological Survey Professional Paper 820, 1973.)

for elements like uranium and thorium and has been used successfully in Japan for estimating their reserves.

Sulfides commonly contain economic quantities of metals like copper, nickel, lead, cobalt, and zinc. One of the reasons these minerals are commonly called *ore* is that they can be easily separated from the silicate-oxide barren, or *gangue*, minerals. The type of bond by which the specific commodity is incorporated into minerals is extremely important. Figure 1–4 illustrates the importance of bonding in minerals and rocks. Nickel (Ni)* is used as the example. Nickel occurs in nature as positively charged Ni^{2+}, which is incorporated into minerals where this positive charge is balanced by the appropriate negative charge. For example, in the olivine minerals Ni^{2+} can occur in the same sites as magnesium (Mg^{2+}) and iron (Fe^{2+}); the total positive charge is balanced by the negative charge on the silicon tetrahedron, SiO_4^{4-}. Thus we would write the formula for this particular olivine as

$$(Mg, Fe, Ni)_2 SiO_4$$

---

*The chemical symbol for each element will be indicated as it is introduced.

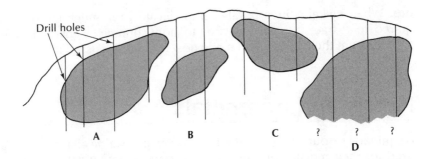

FIGURE 1–4 Importance of metal bonding in minerals. Assume that the total area shown here is essentially all gabbroic rocks with a relatively high nickel content. Also assume that the highest nickel contents are found in zones **A**, **B**, **C**, and **D**; *only* in zones **A** and **D** is the nickel found in *sulfide* minerals. One of the reasons these minerals are commonly called ore is that they can be easily separated from the silicate-oxide barren, or *gangue*, minerals. In zones **B** and **C** if the nickel is bonded in *silicate* minerals, then the cost of recovery would be too high to qualify the rock as ore, even though the nickel content is as high as in zones **A** and **D**. Thus the type of bond by which the specific commodity is incorporated into minerals is extremely important.

Indeed such nickeliferous olivines are common in many mafic to ultramafic rocks* in the absence of sulfur (S). When sulfur is present, however, nickel is preferentially incorporated into sulfide minerals (i.e., those minerals with S^{2-} as the species that balances the positive charge on Ni^{2+}). Elements in their charged (ionic) form which show preference for sulfur instead of silicates or oxides are known as *chalcophile*. Included in this list are iron, nickel, lead, zinc, molybdenum, and mercury, among others. When both nickel and sulfur are present in a silicate rock, the following general partitioning is observed:

$$\frac{\text{Nickel content in sulfide}}{\text{Nickel content in silicate}} > 1$$

In Figure 1–4 we look at a hypothetical mafic rock known as gabbro (plutonic equivalent of basalt), which contains abundant olivine in addition to pyroxenes and plagioclase feldspar. The distribution of nickel is assumed to be uniform throughout the rock, but the distribution of sulfur is uneven. An important fact is that it is easier to break the bond between Ni^{2+} and S^{2-} than that between Ni^{2+} and $1/2(SiO_4)^{4-}$. Stated another way, less energy is required to recover nickel from a sulfide than from a silicate. Hence, for the hypothetical case shown in Figure 1–4, only in those areas where nickel is incorporated into sulfides is the rock truly an

---

*Mafic rocks are those with 45–55 percent SiO_2 content; ultramafic rocks contain less than 45 percent SiO_2.

ore. When nickel is incorporated into silicates, too much energy is required to extract it, and it is sub- to noneconomic. Separating metal sulfides from their silicate and oxide host rocks is discussed in Chapter 2.

Metals and Nonmetals

For mineral resources we use the term *metal* to describe elements that are used for their metallic properties (i.e., conductivity, ductility); the term *nonmetals* refers to those elements and their compounds not used for their metallic properties. Thus sodium (Na), while a metal, is used commercially in sodium compounds based on nonmetallic properties. Oil, gas, and coal are nonmetals, as are potash (KCl), gypsum ($CaSO_4 \cdot 2H_2O$), sand and gravel, cement, borax, sulfur (S), nitrogen (N), and phosphorus (P). The annual world consumption of nonmetals is substantially greater than metallic elements, as the following quantities show:

> Carbon (C): 1–10 billion tons
>
> Sodium (Na) and iron (Fe): 0.1–1 billions tons
>
> Nitrogen (N), oxygen (O), sulfur (S), potassium (K), and calcium (Ca): 10–100 million tons

Only below 10 million tons do we encounter the metals which attract so much glamour, including zinc (Zn), copper (Cu), lead (Pb), magnesium (Mg), chromium (Cr), aluminum (Al), plus the nonmetals hydrogen (H), fluorine (F), phosphorus (P), and barium (Ba)—all in the category of 1 to 10 million tons per year. Thus iron is the only metal ranked in the top eight elements in order of consumption. Carbon is ranked first because of our great consumption of fossil fuels. Except for iron, the top eight elements (N, K, Ca, Na, O, S, Fe, and C) are consumed largely in agriculture and related industries. Not listed here are the tremendous amounts of compounds such as sand, gravel, and other types of industrial rocks.

Minimum Anticipated Cumulative Demand

The acronym **MACD** has been used to describe resource availability since 1973, when it was first introduced by the U.S. Geological Survey. MACD is the *minimum anticipated cumulative demand* for a particular resource for the period from 1975 to 2000. The following Roman numerals indicate resource availabilities and are assigned to a resource according to its multiple of the MACD:

I = 10 or more times MACD
II = 2–10 times MACD
III = 0.75–2 times MACD
IV = 0.35–0.75 times MACD
V = 0.10–0.35 times MACD
VI = less than 0.10 times MACD

Table 1–1 shows the MACDs for some common elements and compounds.

In Table 1–1, an assignment of NE for undiscovered resources may be by very different lines of reasoning for different commodities. In the case of aluminum, we are optimistic that technology will allow us to extract the metal from clays or low-grade bauxites by the year 2000. Hence this NE may be revised to I in the next decade or so. For gold (Au), which is used for purposes of trade payment, resource figures may fluctuate greatly. Gold will continue to be recovered as a by-product of copper mining; but note that copper falls into category III. We may import copper to meet our needs rather than mine our own resources. If, on the other hand, we mine U.S. copper only then increased gold production will also result. Hence a MACD figure in the second column of Table 1–1 could be either III or IV (or V?) depending on the copper market. Similarly, the

TABLE 1–1 Resource availabilities by MACD.

Commodity	Identified Resources	Undiscovered Resources
Aluminum	II	NE*
Asbestos	V	VI
Barite	II	II
Chromium	VI	V
Copper	III	III
Fluorine	V	V
Gold	III	NE
Gypsum	I	I
Iron	II	I
Molybdenum	I	I
Nickel	III	NE
Phosphate	II	I
Sand and Gravel	III	NE
Sulfur	I	I
Titanium	II	II
Uranium	II	III
Vanadium	II	NE
Zinc	II	II

*NE=not estimated
SOURCE: U.S. Geological Survey, Professional Paper 820, 1973.

INTRODUCTION

extent of uranium (U) mining in the latter part of the twentieth century is unknown. If it will be large, then vanadium (V), which must be separated from the uranium during milling, may receive a MACD of II. If uranium mining should decline for unforeseen reasons, then the production of vanadium will also fall and a MACD rating of III might result. There is hope that improved technology will allow the recovery of nickel from weathered, nickeliferous rocks. In that case the second column of Table 1–1 might be III; otherwise the MACD value for nickel will more likely be IV. The availability of sand and gravel is uncertain because there is relatively little prospecting for this valuable commodity. We also need ways to economically recover and transport the huge sand and gravel accumulations in the nearshore parts of the ocean basins; if this can be done, then the MACD may well be I. If not, the MACD will more likely be III—that is, roughly enough to meet demands but not enough to make us complacent about the resource situation.

Industrial materials, especially sand and gravel, cement, and clays are the largest-tonnage commodity in the United States and, next to iron and steel, the most valuable commodity (exclusive of fossil fuels). Supplies appear to be adequate for the remainder of the twentieth century, but careful urban planning will be necessary in the twenty-first century. There are too many examples of poor planning that has rendered good-quality sand and gravel deposits useless and has created unnecessary transportation problems in urban areas in some parts of the country.

MACD figures can be misleading if we attempt to use them on a worldwide basis. The uncertainty is due in part to the uneven distribution of resources, to uneven population density, to varying degrees of industrialization throughout the world, and thus to widely differing per capita consumption. The United States, for example, with less than 10 percent of the world's population has a per capita consumption (i.e., a country's annual gross consumption of a commodity divided by its population) four to five times that of any other industrialized nation or continent. Should Asia and Africa rise to the U.S. level of per capita consumption, then these continents would find it difficult to export anything. Yet the United States relies heavily on imports for many commodities. Further, mass starvation and energy shortages may confront us in the twenty-first century. If calculations by the National Research Council–National Academy of Sciences are correct,* then the world's maximum capacity to produce food for its population may be reached by the mid–twenty-first century. If we add to this the probability that oil and gas resources will have peaked early in the twenty-first century and that many mineral resources will have been mined out, then the entire world will face a crisis. This rather pessimistic view is based on the following assumptions: con-

---

*National Research Council–National Academy of Sciences, *The Earth and Human Affairs* (San Francisco: Canfield Press, 1972).

tinued high rates of population growth, high rates of food consumption, rapid industrialization of essentially unindustrialized countries, no new major mineral deposit discoveries, and failure to use nuclear or alternate (to fossil fuel) energy sources. Therefore, MACD figures may be rather drastically revised for the twenty-first century. There are simply too many uncertainties at this time to warrant MACD projections beyond the year 2000. Furthermore, world MACD figures must be determined and integrated with domestic figures.

Mineral Resource Recovery

Where and how we recover some of our mineral resources is also important. When relatively large amounts of a mineral resource occur close to the surface of the earth, open pit mining is used. Where high-grade ore occurs at some depth, a mine shaft may be sunk and *drifts* (tunnels) run from the main shaft to the ore zones. In some cases ore is of a high grade, but spotty and not thought to be economically recoverable by either open-pit or underground methods. If, as in the case for uranium or copper, the ore minerals can be dissolved in place by acid or alkaline leach solutions, then solution mining may be undertaken. These topics will be discussed in Chapters 2 and 8.

Many mineral resources occur in rocks of a specific type or age. Commonly, many ore deposits are found within one spatial-temporal setting, which may be referred to as a *metallogenic province*. The porphyry copper belt in the western part of both North and South America is one such well-defined province, as is the sedimentary copper belt in Zambia-Zaire. Other examples include tin (Sn) provinces in Peru-Bolivia and Korea–Southeast Asia. Most metallogenic provinces have several characteristics in common: alignment to major tectonic elements (e.g., subduction zone traces), igneous rocks, rocks of equal age, and approximately equivalent chemistry.

Where open or restricted (continental) sea waters have evaporated, corresponding marine or nonmarine evaporite deposits result. The former are valuable for potash, gypsum, and halite; the latter for sodium carbonates, sulfates, and borax. Both are interlayered with limestones and are commonly associated with petroliferous matter and, less frequently, metal sulfide deposits. Other marine sedimentary rocks are rich in phosphorus (e.g., in areas such as Florida, Tennessee, and Utah), while still others may contain economic concentrations of metals. Of the elements crucial to the agricultural industry, potassium as potash (KCl) is recovered from marine evaporites; phosphate rock is recovered from apatite-rich marine shales; sulfur is most abundant in cap rocks of certain marine evaporites; and nitrogen is extracted from the atmosphere.

Fuels and Alternative Energy Sources

Fuels deserve special mention. While coal reserves are widespread in the United States and are apparently abundant elsewhere in the Northern Hemisphere (see Figure 7–14), they also require the stripping of vast acreage and pose a potentially major threat to the environment. Oil and gas reserves will probably peak early in the twenty-first century on a worldwide basis. Since roughly 30 percent of our energy needs are for transportation—and these needs can only be met by oil and gas—then substitutes for oil and gas must be found for industrial, commercial, and household uses. Coal can be used locally for this purpose, but in the long range may be impractical for many economical and environmental reasons (see Chapter 7). Alternate sources of power are as yet either subeconomic (solar), too restricted geographically (geothermal), not yet developed (fusion), or too sparse (hydroelectric).

We have at our disposal a well-designed nuclear capability, yet some of the public are reluctant to accept nuclear power. Part of this reluctance is due to the "atom bomb syndrome" (i.e., some of the public still erroneously believe that a reactor is like a bomb); while part is due to the problem of radioactive waste. Lost somewhere in the arguments about nuclear reactors is the fact that radioactive wastes from the defense industry and some from commercial reactors are already here, and the former, at least, will continue to accumulate. (The ratio of military to commercial waste is roughly three to one.) It has already been demonstrated that fission-produced radioactive waste can indeed be retained in geologic settings. The Oklo uranium deposit in Gabon (Plate 1) contains 2-billion-year-old uranium which sustained a fission reaction for more than 500,000 years. Most of the waste products, from high-level to low-level, are still present as the stable daughter products of radioactive decay. Since we worry about repositories for some 250,000 years, then the Oklo deposit has shown us that radioactive wastes can be isolated for 7200 times this length of time!

The advantage of a breeder reactor is that it creates more fuel than is first fed into it; but its main disadvantage is that it produces plutonium-239, one of the ingredients for making atomic weapons. Obviously, we must exercise careful control in monitoring the nuclear industry, yet the public must learn that this is a realistic energy alternative when faced with certain oil and gas shortages and the disadvantages of switching to a coal-based energy plan. Refer to Chapters 7 and 8 for a more detailed discussion of this problem.

Hydroelectric power generation has been with us for a long time, and indeed it will continue to play a significant, but small role. In short, water is too valuable a commodity (see Chapter 3) to be routinely used for power generation. Furthermore, many of the best areas for water

FUELS AND ALTERNATIVE ENERGY SOURCES

PLATE 1

View of the Oklo uranium mine, Republic of Gabon. This view shows a small open pit mine and several persons who attended the 1975 Conference on the Oklo Phenomenon (Natural Fission Reactor) sponsored by the International Atomic Energy Agency, the French Atomic Energy Commission, and the Republic of Gabon. Nature sustained a fission reaction at this site some two billion years ago.

power generation are in wilderness areas, making it neither economic nor wise to even consider using them for hydroelectric power. Similarly, geothermal energy will be important when natural steam fields are located near metropolitan areas (The Geysers near San Francisco, for example) and when transmission of electrical energy over great distances becomes more efficient. Thus the potential of geothermal energy in many remote areas in the western United States must await major technological breakthroughs in power transmission. The *hot dry rock* (HDR) program (see Chapter 7) is potentially of great importance. Unlike the western United States, the rocks in the northeastern United States possess normal heat flow. If the HDR method is employed there, drilling to a depth of 4 to 5 kilometers will return warm water (not steam) from cold water injected into the earth. Along the Atlantic seaboard roughly from New York to Bangor, Maine, space heating accounts for 40 percent of all energy used. The warm water generated by the HDR method could be used for space heating, thus saving tremendous amounts of oil, gas, and other conventional energy resources.

Solar energy is being used, but it is at present only of local importance. More and more buildings, including industrial and commercial buildings, are being designed to use energy from the sun. Yet even the most optimistic advocates of solar energy admit that this resource will make but a minor dent in the total energy picture by the year 2000. Quite simply, solar energy is too expensive to compete with natural oil and gas, coal, and nuclear energy. Fusion energy is another goal for the future; optimistically, it is hoped that experimental plants will be on-line by about the year 2030.

Oil shale is another virtually untapped resource. The term *oil shale* is a misnomer, as the rock is actually a kerogen-bearing marlstone* formed under nonmarine, near-evaporite conditions. It resembles shale because it is dark colored (due to its kerogen content) and finely laminated. The amount of petroliferous material stored in these *oil-marlstones* in nonmarine formations in Utah, Colorado, and Wyoming is impressive; the U.S. Geological Survey includes two trillion barrels of oil in its estimate. But there is a drawback to this encouraging picture. Oil-marlstones are located in arid to semiarid isolated areas, and recovery of their oil is not now economic. One of the main problems is a shortage of water. Some estimates indicate that mining and processing require three to four barrels of water for every barrel of oil recovered, and these water resources are not available. To transport the kerogen-bearing rocks elsewhere is less economic than transporting equivalent tonnages of coal, which is, in turn, subeconomic at best. Furthermore, there is potential damage to the environment by mining; and some of the oil-marlstones occur in wilderness areas. We will continue to study the promising *in situ* methods of oil production, in which oil can be produced from beneath the ground by dissolving kerogen from the host rock and pumping it to the surface. A bonus for oil-marlstones is that they contain large amounts of the mineral *dawsonite*, a sodium-aluminum carbonate. This highly soluble mineral could help pay for the oil production because of its high and easily recoverable aluminum content.

Water

Water resources comprise only that percentage of total precipitation which is withdrawn for use by people. In the United States this amounts to only 9 percent. Of this small fraction, most is used for irrigation and for industries; the remainder is used for municipalities. The National Research Council–National Academy of Sciences estimates that the United States must find ways to use close to 80 percent of available stream and lake waters by the year 2000, as opposed to about 30 percent now

---

*Marlstone is a variety of rock that is rich in calcium carbonate.

withdrawn.* To do this, recycling of industrial waters and other conservation measures must be expanded. However, conservation measures have not been effective enough to keep pace with projected increases in withdrawals. Desalination of ocean water along both seaboards and of brines from some areas will help; but desalination is expensive, and industrial and agricultural groups have not been cooperative in funding or using experimental systems.

It cannot be emphasized strongly enough that water, in terms of both quantity and quality, is the most important resource in the world. Without adequate water, agriculture and the entire population suffer. We must enforce existing environmental controls or implement new ones to ensure an adequate supply of potable water as the growth of this nation and the world continues.

*A. Wolman, Water Resources Publication 1000–B (Washington, D.C.; National Research Council–National Academy of Sciences, 1962).

Ores, Production, and Mining

Elements and Ores

Of the 92 naturally occurring elements, nine (oxygen, silicon, aluminum, iron, calcium, magnesium, sodium, potassium, and titanium) make up over 90 percent of all the rocks of the earth's crust. Oxygen and silicon together account for almost 75 percent by weight (47.5 percent and 27.5 percent, respectively). Oxygen bonded in rocks and minerals accounts for 94 percent of their volume.

Of these nine elements, none is readily available as an economically recoverable resource in the common rock-forming minerals. This is because all nine elements are found in rocks and minerals as *ions*, which are bonded together in different ways. Ions are merely atoms that have gained or lost electrons. When formed, every atom has an equal number of negatively charged electrons and positively charged protons; the atom has no net positive or negative charge. Should an atom lose one or more electrons, it becomes a positively charged ion, called a *cation* because it will be attracted to the cathode in an electrolytic cell. Atoms that gain electrons take on a negative charge and are called *anions* because they would be attracted to the positively charged anode in the same cell. Of the nine elements listed above, only oxygen forms an anion (O^{2-}) while the others form cations (Si^{4+}, Al^{3+}, Fe^{2+}, Fe^{3+}, Mg^{2+}, Ca^{2+}, Na^+, K^+, and Ti^{4+}). See Appendix 2 for more information.

Oxygen and silicon are so abundant that they combine to form the silicon tetrahedron (SiO_4^{4-}), comprised of a central ion of Si^{4+} surrounded by four O^{2-} ions. This structure is possible because the radius for the Si^{4+} ion is only 0.35 angstrom (1 angstrom = 10^{-8} centimeters), and each O^{2-} ion is 1.35 angstroms in radius. The net charge on this silicon tetrahedron is −4:

$$4(-2) + 1(+4) = -4$$

This negative charge is usually balanced by the other major elements in their ionic form found in natural compounds.

A few major rock-forming minerals constitute over 99 percent of the rocks found in the earth's crust. Shown in Table 2–1, they are written in simplest form as compounds. At first glance, this list of minerals looks quite complex. When we remember that there are more than 2500 minerals found in nature, then the few listed in Table 2–1 are impressive because they are so much more abundant than all the others.

TABLE 2–1   Major rock-forming minerals.

Mineral	Formula
Olivine	$(Mg, Fe)_2SiO_4$
Pyroxene	
(a) enstatite	$MgSiO_3$
(b) diopside	$CaMgSi_2O_6$
(c) augite	$(Ca, Na) (Mg, Fe^{2+}, Fe^{3+}, Al) (Al, Si)_2 O_6$
Amphibole	
(a) hornblende	$(Ca, Na)_{2-3}(Mg, Fe^{2+}, Fe^{3+}, Al)_5(Al, Si)_8(O)_{22}(OH)_2$
Potassium feldspars (sanidine, microcline, orthoclase)	$KAlSi_3O_8$
Plagioclase—a mixture of	
(a) albite	$NaAlSi_3O_8$
(b) anorthite	$CaAl_2Si_2O_8$
Micas	
(a) biotite	$K(Mg, Fe)_3AlSi_3O_{10}(OH)_2$
(b) muscovite	$K(Al_2)AlSi_3O_{10}(OH)_2$
Quartz	SiO_2

It is noteworthy that titanium (as Ti^{4+}) has not specifically been included in any of the minerals listed so far. This is because titanium is usually hidden in silicate minerals such as augite and hornblende, where due to its similar size (i.e., ionic radius) it can substitute for Fe^{3+} or, less commonly, for Fe^{2+} or Mg^{2+}. Owing to its large charge and size relative to Si^{4+} and Al^{3+}, titanium commonly forms accessory minerals where it is a dominant ion—ilmenite ($FeTiO_3$) and sphene ($CaTiSiO_5$), for example. Other important accessory minerals are listed in Table 2–2.

TABLE 2–2   Accessory minerals.

Mineral	Formula	Comments
Apatite	$Ca_5(PO_4)_3(OH, F)$	Contains phosphorus
Pyrite	FeS_2	Main sulfur-bearing mineral in igneous rocks
Calcite	$CaCO_3$	Most abundant mineral containing carbon (Note: Organic carbon from plant and animal remains not included here)
Magnetite	Fe_3O_4	Common in igneous rocks.

Only in the mineral olivine is the net charge of -4 balanced by a simple charge of $+4$. In most other minerals one or more corners of the silicon tetrahedron are shared with other tetrahedra to form chains (pyroxenes and amphiboles), sheets (micas and clay minerals), and three-dimensional stacks (so-called framework structures such as feldspars and quartz). All minerals with one or more silicon tetrahedra are known as *silicates*. If silicon is absent and only oxygen is present as an anion, then the mineral is called an *oxide*. Hematite (Fe_2O_3) and magnetite (Fe_3O_4) are oxides.

When carbon or phosphorus combines with oxygen to form an anion such as CO_3^{2-} (carbonate ion) or PO_4^{3-} (phosphate ion), then carbonate minerals such as *calcite* ($CaCO_3$, the main mineral in limestone) or *dolomite* ($CaMg(CO_3)_2$) will be found, as will phosphate minerals such as *apatite*, $Ca_5(PO_4)_3(OH, F)$. Sulfur usually occurs in nature with charges of -2, 0, or $+6$. Most *sulfides* have a charge of -2 (e.g., the lead ore galena, PbS). Pyrite (FeS_2) is a notable exception: while the Fe^{2+} ion has an overall charge of $+2$, one sulfur is -2 and the other is zero; yet the electrons move back and forth between the sulfur species so rapidly that it is impossible to predict which is -2 and which is zero. This is an academic point, however, because *pyrite* is the most common accessory sulfide mineral found in common rocks. Native sulfur is common in hot springs areas near volcanic areas or in other areas where hot waters or bacterial action have caused its formation. The ion S^{6+} is usually found in combination with oxygen as SO_4^{2-} (sulfate ion). The well-known minerals *barite* ($BaSO_4$) and *gypsum* ($CaSO_4 \cdot 2H_2O$) are good examples of sulfate minerals; both are of significant economic importance. Another group of anions in nature is the halides (Cl^-, F^-, and Br^-). The first of these is found in common table salt, the mineral *halite* (NaCl). Potassium chloride (KCl) is the most important ore for potassium, as will be shown in Chapter 5. The most important mineral with the fluoride ion (F^-) is the mineral *fluorite* (CaF_2), or calcium fluoride. Other lesser-known compounds will be mentioned as necessary. Except where noted (e.g., Fe^{2+}, Fe^{3+}), all of the ions listed in the preceding formulas are assumed to possess their most common charge.

We have now listed most of the essential and common accessory minerals found in igneous rocks. How elements other than the most abundant nine listed earlier are incorporated into these and a few other common minerals is of prime interest, because this is the key to an element's economic importance. The charge (valence), ionic radius, and affinity for sulfur rather than the oxygen (in oxides or silicates) must all be considered. A simple example will illustrate this point. Copper (Cu) occurs in nature as the native element or as Cu^+ and Cu^{2+}. Although the Cu^+ ion has the same ionic radius as Na^+, copper has a stronger affinity for sulfur than for oxygen or silicates. Hence Cu^+ will not be concentrated in the plagioclase albite ($NaAlSi_3O_8$) but will be concentrated instead in accessory pyrite (FeS_2). This is fortunate because pyrite can be readily separated from silicates such as albite and chemically processed to extract copper. If the copper were locked up in albite, it would take so much energy to break down the mineral and to process it for copper extraction that it would not be economic. Elements are therefore commonly classified as to whether they have an affinity for sulfur (*chalcophile*) or oxygen as oxides or silicates (*lithophile*), or whether they occur as gases in the earth's atmosphere (*atmophile*) or as the native element (*siderophile*). Table 2–3 shows these classifications for the common elements.

TABLE 2–3 Classification of common elements.

CHALCOPHILE
  Copper, lead, zinc, iron, nickel, cobalt, cadmium, mercury, arsenic, antimony, selenium, tellurium, sulfur, molybdenum

LITHOPHILE
  Silicon, oxygen, aluminum, iron, sodium, potassium, magnesium, calcium, barium, beryllium, strontium, titanium, zirconium, thorium, uranium, chromium, vanadium, niobium, tantalum, phosphorus, boron, cesium, lithium, hydrogen, fluorine, iodine, chlorine, bromine, carbon

SIDEROPHILE
  Iron, cobalt, nickel, gold, silver, copper, platinum, palladium, osmium, iridium, rhenium

ATMOPHILE
  Nitrogen, oxygen, argon, helium, neon, krypton, xenon, hydrogen

Some elements are placed in more than one category in the table. Iron, the fourth most abundant element in the earth's crust, is chalcophile, lithophile, and siderophile; but it occurs only rarely as native iron in terrestrial materials. (Native iron-nickel alloy is common in meteorites and will be discussed in Chapter 4.) More commonly iron is concentrated in silicates and sulfides. Iron shows a strong preference for sulfur; thus pyrite is a very common accessory mineral in igneous rocks. But there is much more iron than sulfur present, so the bulk of the iron is incorporated into silicates such as biotite, pyroxenes, or amphiboles; yet *none* of these minerals is an iron ore. Weathering and other processes must, in effect, work overtime to reprocess these original iron-bearing minerals into materials suitable for iron ore. (An exception is low-grade taconite, which is discussed in Chapter 4.)

An ore is a substance (usually rock or mineral) from which a specific element or group of elements can be profitably extracted. A famous Russian geochemist, A.E. Fersman, used the term *clarke** as the concentration of an element in the earth's crust. This was later modified by the Russian geochemist W. J. Vernadsky, who introduced the term *concentration clarke*. This concentration factor, if met, would indicate that a particular element had been concentrated to the point where it could be profitably extracted from a rock or mineral. Thus manganese, with a crustal abundance of 0.1 percent, is said to have a clarke of 0.1. In a mineral such as pyrolusite (MnO_2) the concentration clarke for manganese is 630; that is, pyrolusite is 63 percent manganese by weight. Because most ore minerals such as pyrolusite are mixed with other barren (or *gangue*) minerals, the true *concentration factor* would be different from the concentration clarke in any particular mineral. A few concentration factors for some common elements are given in Table 2–4.

TABLE 2–4 Concentrations of common elements.

Element	Clarke	Minimum % for Economic Extraction	Concentration Factor
Aluminum	8.1	About 30	4
Iron	5.0	About 30	6
Copper	0.007	About 0.5	70
Chromium	0.02	About 30	1500
Lead	0.0016	About 3.5	2400
Uranium	0.0002	About 0.08	400

While only a relatively small concentration factor is needed for economic extraction of abundant elements such as aluminum and iron, there are apparent discrepancies between *concentration clarke* and *concentration factor* for elements such as chromium, lead, and uranium. For the extraction of chromium to be profitable, the percentage of chromium must be high (30 percent) because it is contained in the complex oxide mineral chromite ($FeCr_2O_4$), which requires much energy to break

*After F.W. Clarke, a famous American geochemist.

it down and to remove and purify the chromium. Thus an impure chromite—that is, one with more iron—would probably not be suitable for economic recovery of chromium. Lead, found in sulfide minerals, can be separated from silicates with relative ease. (Galena, PbS, is the most common lead sulfide.) Although lead is less than one-tenth as abundant as chromium, its concentration factor is only greater than that for chromium by a factor of 1.6 (2400/1500). Uranium's unique chemistry allows very low grade ore to be efficiently processed so that, despite a clarke of only 0.0002, ore with as little as 0.05 percent (or less, based on 1979 prices) can be profitably mined. Hence the concentration factor is relatively low, because separation of the uranium minerals from the gangue is not necessary during metal extraction (as is the case for copper, lead, and chromium). The uranium is oxidized in the crushed ore and removed and purified by solution chemistry in a complex but straightforward process (discussed in Chapter 2).

Trace element distribution in rocks is of the utmost importance. Chromium, which is very similar to iron (Fe^{3+}) in distribution, is usually incorporated into iron-bearing minerals and thus is subeconomic. Lead, being chalcophile, will usually be concentrated in sulfides which are easily separated from silicates. Because of its large ionic radius (1.04 angstroms for U^{4+}), uranium is difficult to incorporate into the rock-forming minerals; thus, because it is lithophile, it is concentrated in minute crystals and along grain boundaries as uranium oxide or silicate. Furthermore, it takes less energy to oxidize uranium in insoluble form (U^{4+}) to soluble form (U^{6+}) than it does to oxidize iron as Fe^{2+} (in pyroxene, for example) to Fe^{3+} (in reddish minerals such as hematite, Fe_2O_3). Thus if reddish-yellow iron staining (analogous to rust) is noted on rock outcrops, it is safe to assume that most of the near-surface uranium has been leached from the rocks as well. This leached uranium (as U^{6+} in some form) is transported into the rocks, where conditions will be reversed and U^{6+} will be reduced to U^{4+}; thus very pure uranium minerals will precipitate more abundantly than in the rocks in which they were first formed. Ideally, there should be a fifth column added to Table 2–4 to reflect the ease by which the concentration factor is reached. Natural processes, such as weathering, must work harder to reach the concentration factor of 4 for aluminum than to reach the concentration factor of 400 for uranium.

It is not rock chemistry, however, that dictates whether or not ore can be mined. The geologic setting should be such that not too much waste rock (overburden) must be removed; and the ore must be located in areas not too remote from markets so that transportation and related costs are not excessive. In short, the economics of extracting the potential ore must be carefully evaluated. Consider the example of a small but rich deposit of some metal located well above the Arctic Circle. If this hypothetical deposit were located more favorably, it would be economic.

PLATE 2

*Core box of very high grade uranium ore from Key Lake,
Saskatchewan. This particular ore contains up to 40 percent uranium
and 40 percent nickel in places.*

As it is, the assumed amount of ore would probably be too small and the costs too great to warrant mining and shipping.

Another example could be the numerous small lead-zinc deposits of the Mississippi Valley which also contain high concentrations of mercury, an element in short supply. If rock chemistry alone were considered, these ores would possess enough mercury to warrant their exploitation. Yet the ores are difficult to treat and recovery costs are high. Also, most of these deposits are located in urban areas, agricultural areas, or in areas where mining would affect the water quality of streams and rivers if not carefully controlled. Hence the costs to ensure environmental protection would add to the already high costs for recovery. Since the deposits are too small to warrant economic recovery of lead and zinc, reliance on these two metals to cut costs of mecury recovery is unlikely. Thus, this resource must await technological breakthroughs for profitable extraction without environmental damage.

Rock which contains 0.5 percent copper is not necessarily considered ore. If the copper is present in sulfides, then it may be ore; but if the copper is present in oxides, it will usually cost too much to extract and thus is not considered ore. In the latter case, high concentrations in oxidized rocks warrant further exploration by deeper drilling; that is, if the rocks are less oxidized, the possibility of finding copper in sulfides is greater. The nature of the rocks drilled should be very carefully examined. If pyrite (a sulfide, FeS_2) with a low copper content is encountered, then the higher concentrations of copper in the oxidized rocks above it must be due to fixation there from some other original source or due to impoverishment of sulfur in the rocks. The present-day economic geologist uses many tools for exploration and very sophisticated techniques to evaluate rocks for their economic potential.

By-products

When copper is extracted from its ore, other chalcophile elements are removed. Because they may pose environmental hazards if dumped into streams or air, these by-products must be carefully removed and sold or safely stored.

The United States has an abundance of molybdenum (Mo) in the mineral molybdenite (MoS_2). The concentration clarke for molybdenum in molybdenite is 600. Yet 25 percent of U.S. molybdenum production comes from by-products from the copper industry, even though the molybdenum content of the copper ore is only 0.01 percent. This is because tremendous amounts of copper ore are processed and the molybdenum, which is chalcophile and thus concentrated in the same sulfides which contain the copper, is readily separated from the copper. Furthermore, like uranium, molybdenum is carried in oxidizing solutions as Mo^{6+} complexes and is reduced to Mo^{4+} when U^{6+} is reduced to U^{4+}. Thus molybdenum is a by-product—in small quantities—from uranium mining as well. The importance of by-products from the mining of other major commodities will be explained in the chapters to follow.

Mineral Production in the United States

We will now look briefly at some data for U.S. mineral production, exports and imports. As shown in Table 2–5, while U.S. production of mineral fuels increased 100 percent between 1970 and 1974 and exports increased 138 percent, the value of imports in the same period increased a staggering 956 percent! Furthermore, the ratio of imports to combined production and export for mineral fuel in 1970 was only 6.8 percent; yet in 1974 this ratio was 27.5 percent—a fourfold increase! The same trend is noted for nonmetals and metals, but not at the same pace. These data demonstrate convincingly that the United States cannot, without risk of severe inflation, continue to import fuels. As we will see, even if an inflationary path is followed the petroleum fuels will peak by about the end of the twentieth century. This means that such a path is doubly damning: (1) the

TABLE 2–5   Crude mineral production, exports, and imports (value in millions of dollars).

Mineral Group	1970			1974		
	Production	Exports	Imports	Production	Exports	Imports
Metals and non-metals (no fuels)						
Nonmetals	5,712	225	551	8,682	526	1,158
Metals	3,928	322	1,249	5,552	343	1,714
Mineral fuels	20,152	1,120	1,567	40,921	2,664	16,545

SOURCE: U. S. Bureau of Mines, *Minerals Yearbook*, 1974.

decreased value of the dollar will reduce our bargaining power at the international level; and (2) money which could be used to develop energy alternatives to petroleum will have been wasted. While this sounds harsh, it is realistic and well documented.

Another interesting way to view the value of U.S. mineral production is by state. It is commonly assumed that the wealth of a state goes hand in hand with its mineral wealth. The data for selected states are shown in Table 2–6.

California, Illinois, Ohio, Pennsylvania, and New York are listed in Table 2–6 primarily because of their high populations. It is interesting to note that the per capita rankings for these states are all low. Figures can be very deceiving, however. New Mexico, for example, has a per capita ranking of 3, yet in 1970 the per capita *income* in New Mexico ranked forty-ninth! Similarly, some states with high mineral production value rankings, such as West Virginia and Kentucky (which is ranked eleventh), are actually quite poor in terms of per capita income. These data illustrate that even though mineral commodities are located in specific states, "wealth" will not necessarily remain within those states. When valuable minerals are in low-population states, per capita production dollar values are usually high (as in New Mexico, Utah, Arizona, Alaska, and Wyoming). The main contributing commodities for low-population states are usually easy to recognize but not necessarily easy to predict. If, for example, the coal industry should be drastically cut back in West Virginia, then that state's ranking would also decrease drastically. (In 1974 coal accounted for 92 percent of West Virginia's mineral production value.) Similarly, Alaska relies heavily on its petroleum industry, Arizona on copper, Pennsylvania on coal, and so on. Louisiana and Texas both contain abundant petroleum (gas, oil, and natural gas liquids) plus other resources. As an example of how the value of a state's mineral production values may change as a function of commodity, examine the data for New Mexico shown in Table 2–7.

24

TABLE 2–6 Value of mineral production for selected states (1970).

State	Population (thousands)	Value (thousands)	Per Capita Dollars	Rank
Wyoming	332	$ 1,437,200	$4,329	1
Louisiana	3,643	8,146,578	2,237	2
New Mexico	1,016	1,941,544	1,911	3
Alaska	300	488,437	1,495	4
West Virginia	1,744	2,403,177	1,378	5
Texas	11,197	13,711,144	1,225	6
Utah	1,059	952,045	899	7
Arizona	1,771	1,562,234	882	8
Oklahoma	2,559	2,123,690	830	9
Montana	694	574,801	828	10
California	19,953	2,797,080	140	26
Illinois	11,114	1,149,210	103	29
New York	18,237	440,573	24	44
Ohio	10,652	1,107,670	104	28
Pennsylvania	11,794	2,374,512	201	21

SOURCE: U.S. Bureau of Mines, *Minerals Yearbook*, 1974.

TABLE 2–7 Mineral production in New Mexico: Selected commodities (thousands of dollars).

Commodity	1970	1974
Copper	$ 163,716	$ 303,920
Lead	820	1,064
Natural gas	175,137	390,861
Petroleum (crude)	402,602	712,578
Potash	86,689	128,588
Sand and gravel	7,975	10,605
Uranium	65,517	104,693
Gold	441	2,464
Zinc	4,495	9,897
TOTAL	1,006,285	1,941,544

SOURCE: U.S. Bureau of Mines, *Minerals Yearbook*, 1974.

Of New Mexico's commodities, gold, lead, and zinc will follow the copper market because all are produced as by-products during copper milling and purification. As of 1977 the copper market was less favorable because a glut from many sources led to decreased production for copper, and thus for gold, lead, and zinc. For the fuels, increased production for natural gas, petroleum, and uranium will continue. Eventually gas and oil production will taper off, but newly developed uranium production will continue to increase (and thus increase in dollar value) past the leveling-off point for petroleum products. Potash, however, is a special case. Although production increased drastically between 1971 and 1974, production will decline in the near future because of increased mining costs and the availability of potash from Saskatchewan. This potash is supplied to the northern farming states at lower transportation costs than New Mexico can offer. So although potash reserves are plentiful, production will level off, exports to non-Canadian countries will increase, and Canadian imports will increase. The sand, gravel, and stone industries will thrive as metropolitan areas continue to grow. Because New Mexico has an abundance of mineral commodities, its overall production values will remain high even if one commodity should wane severely for a while. Not all states are so fortunate as New Mexico.

Mining and Other Recovery Methods

The key to recovery of any mineral commodity from the earth is extraction at a profit. Some elements such as bromine and magnesium can be extracted directly from sea water (Chapters 4 and 5); as compounds (e.g., halite, or common table salt) by evaporation of sea water; or from the atmosphere (e.g., nitrogen and argon). Yet most of our mineral resources require extraction from the earth.

Major mining methods include conventional underground mining, open pit mining, and solution mining. Of lesser importance are placer mining and sea floor mining.

Underground Mining

First it must be determined that the element or metal compound is concentrated sufficiently for extraction of the metal during milling. For example, concentrations of copper or nickel in sulfides at minimum ore grade probably would not be sufficient for ore grade if they occurred in silicates or oxides.

Next, a specific mining method is chosen. The diagram in Figure 2–1 shows a case in which open pit mining could not be used because of the very high waste-to-ore ratio that would result. Thus, underground mining is usually undertaken for ore not close to the surface. Examples include copper vein deposits, sporadic uranium deposits, and lode gold deposits. Advantages of this method are (1) once the main shaft is complete, it is relatively inexpensive to develop the underground workings; and (2) detailed drilling from the shaft or tunnels is inexpensive compared with surface drilling.

PLATE 3

Very large drill core (4.5 feet, or 1.35 meters, in diameter) from the Callahan Mine, Harborside, Maine. The large core was drilled for two purposes: (1) as the main shaft excavation for underground operations, and (2) to closely examine the complex rocks in the area which, at the surface, are largely covered by forest, water, or glacial debris.

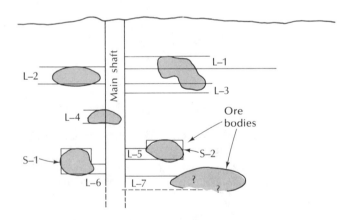

FIGURE 2–1 Underground mining. In this method a main shaft is sunk to a predetermined depth, and tunnels (called *drifts* or *adits*) from this main shaft are used to reach the ore bodies at various levels (L–1, L–2, etc.). When the ore is thicker than the tunnels, stopes (S–1 and S–2) are excavated, provided the rock can withstand excavation or can be supported by other methods.

MINING AND OTHER RECOVERY METHODS

In general, if pockets of ore are close to the same depth, then a vertical or inclined *shaft* is sunk as close as possible to the center of the ore pods (Figure 2–1). *Drifts* (tunnels) off this main shaft are then excavated, usually just under the ore pods so that they can be mined from below or in such a way that ore is removed by *raises* connecting drifts from two or more levels. In mountains, horizontal tunnels called *adits* are driven into the ore body. Occasionally the ore is oriented in such a way that tunnels are driven in at odd angles to extract the ore.

When the ore body is so voluminous that a large volume of rock (far in excess of drift dimension) is extracted, a large "room" called a *stope* is created. If the rock is hard and resistant, stopes may need little accessory support. However, usually the rocks will give way to the overlying pressure of rock cover; cave-ins can be prevented by leaving rock pillars or by erecting supports of timber or other materials. Limiting factors here include the maximum volume of rock that can be extracted

PLATE 4

Head frame of the mine shaft at the Section 30 Mine in the Grants Mineral Belt, New Mexico. High-grade uranium ore is stockpiled in front of the frame awaiting shipment to the mill. The actual mine workings for ore recovery are at a depth of 1000 feet (300 meters) below the surface.

PLATE 5

Covered hoist-head frame for the Fay Shaft in the Eldorado uranium mines in northern Saskatchewan. The underground workings persist to more than 4000 feet (1200 meters).

PLATE 6

Earth-moving shovel used in uranium mining in Wyoming.

without causing a cave-in, regardless of accessory support. Rock pillars are often not feasible because they themselves represent ore-grade rock. In such cases these pillars may be left in place until an area is effectively mined out. Then, one by one, the most distant pillars are removed systematically, progressing toward the main shaft, and the mined-out areas allowed to cave in. This practice is normally only done when such caving will not cause excessive subsidence at the surface and when it has been determined, to the best of the mining engineers' knowledge, that no more ore remains in the outlying limits.

Underground mining is very complex. Not only must maximum efficiency for ore recovery be sought, but safety factors must also be rigorously enforced at all steps. In mines where explosive gases like methane or radioactive gas like radon can accumulate, sophisticated ventilation systems are installed. Even where only nonflammable, nonradioactive particulate matter is involved, good ventilation is essential to assure emergency venting for workers should underground workings between the vent systems and the haulage shafts collapse.

Mine disasters are still too common, especially in coal mines, even though the safety record of underground mining has improved significantly in the last 25 years. Coal mining still presents the greatest immediate hazards from explosions and caving as well as long-term hazards from inhaling carcinogens (including radioactive materials enriched at low levels in coal). Uranium mines have one of the best underground mining safety records because the required workings are less extensive and because radiation and safety regulations are rigidly enforced by the federal government. The potash and salt underground mining industry and the limestone mines can claim safety records close to that of the uranium-mining industry.

Another interesting facet of underground mining is that much of the waste rock is not brought to the surface and dumped. Instead it is used as backfill for support of underground workings where the ore has been mined out.

Open Pit Mining

Open pit mining is used primarily where the ore deposits are relatively close to the surface, the ore is disseminated through the rocks, and the host rock characteristics are such that the walls will be self-supporting.

Deciding whether to mine ore by open pit or underground methods is often difficult. Figure 2–2 shows a hypothetical massive ore body close to the surface. As illustrated, the limits of the ore must be carefully determined prior to excavation. Should too small a pit be cut initially, it is difficult, dangerous, and time consuming to attempt to widen the pit. Conversely, too large a pit is wasteful. Too much rock is excavated and, unlike most underground mining, the waste rock is deposited elsewhere on the surface, causing more disturbance of the original surroundings.

Figure 2–3 shows more hypothetical ore, some of which occurs in smaller bodies, which is not interconnected and has an overall

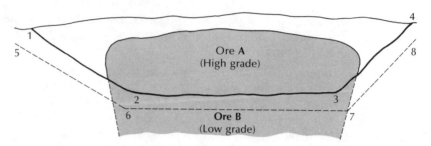

FIGURE 2–2 Open pit mining. One type of open pit mining is illustrated here. The ore body **A** has been outlined by drilling and found to be relatively close to the surface. The solid line 1–2–3–4 indicates the most favorable width-to-depth conditions for the open pit. Although ore continues below the line 1–2–3–4, developing the pit along the dotted line 5–6–7–8 would move too much barren rock and increase mining costs, making ore recovery unprofitable. The more or less uniform body shown is typical of some porphyry copper deposits.

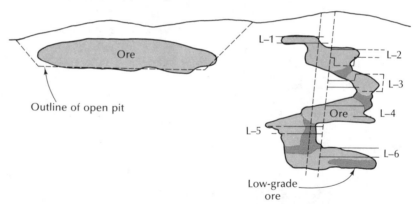

FIGURE 2–3 Economic mining methods. Because ore body **A** is tabular and near the surface, it can be mined by open pit methods, as indicated by the dashed line. At a much greater depth, it would be more profitable to sink a vertical shaft to the ore level and recover the ore by a series of tunnels and larger mined-out areas (stopes) where the ore thickens. Ore body **B**, a more or less discontinuous ore encountered from near the surface to fairly great depths, should be mined by underground methods. Although the initial expense to sink the main shaft is considerable, once the shaft is down it is relatively inexpensive to develop the ore body by drilling underground.

depth-to-width ratio greater than unity. Underground methods must be used to mine this ore body *B* because too large a pit would have to be made to remove the ore by open pit methods. Ore body *A*, because of its massive nature and shallow depth, can be mined by open pit methods.

PLATE 7

Part of the open pit at the Highland uranium mine in the Powder River Basin, Wyoming. Because the ore is located very near the surface, it is economic to recover the ore by open pit methods.

Solution Mining

Occasionally ore that is soluble in either acids or bases occurs in rocks (usually sedimentary rocks) as shown in Figure 2–4. If the ore is widely distributed in one or more layers or is too sporadic to warrant open pit mining, then solution mining may be undertaken.

Solution mining may also be recommended where the ore is of a low grade or the ground too weak to support underground workings. This method's advantages are low capital requirements, negligible rock excavation, and no vast amounts of tailings as waste. Solution mining works best for deposits that cannot be mined by either open pit or underground methods, and care must be taken that all solutions stay within the limits of the ore horizon. In this method several injection wells are drilled into the ore-bearing rock, which must be relatively permeable for the method to work. The ore metal is dissolved and pumped to the surface from several centrally located recovery wells. This method works well for ores that are readily soluble and where the solutions, usually acidic, will not remove much of the gangue. If too much gangue is dissolved, the ore horizon becomes more permeable and dissolved material may be lost into aquifers that provide water for irrigation or consumption. Thus environmental impact must be carefully assessed even though no mechanical

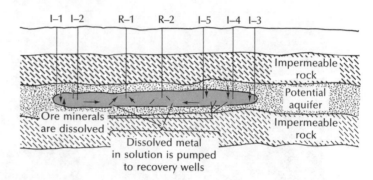

FIGURE 2–4 Solution mining. For some ore, such as copper and uranium ores, the ore minerals can be dissolved by acid- or alkaline-leach injected under pressure through a series of injection wells (I–1 to I–5) and recovered by pumping from recovery wells R–1 and R–2. As shown here, the injection wells surround the recovery wells.

extraction of rock is planned except surface scraping for milling and supporting facilities.

Solution mining has been used on a small scale for many years, sometimes quite by accident. In the 1930s slightly acidic rainwaters percolating over waste from copper mining at Ray, Arizona, dissolved

PLATE 8

Copper precipitation plant in Butte, Montana, in 1956.
(Courtesy of W. E. Elston.)

some of the remaining copper and redeposited it electrolytically on cans in a garbage dump at the end of the waste rock dump. The method was so efficient that for a while a major cost for subsequent copper mining of dump materials was the cost of scrap. Even now solution mining is used in the copper industry, often after fracturing the rocks by explosives to allow natural rain and other waters to infiltrate the rocks more easily and dissolve the copper. The solutions containing copper are channeled down a gradient, where they can be recovered by displacing another metal from scrap. The copper-coated scrap is then milled with ease.

Some low-grade uranium deposits are excellent for solution mining. Acidic solutions dissolve only the uranium minerals, which may constitute only 0.1 percent or less of the rocks, and the uranium is thus removed with little change on the leached rocks. This method does not expose miners to radon inhalation or ingestion of other particulate matter, and no dump materials result. The method works best for small, low-grade deposits where neither underground nor open pit methods are feasible. Again, effects on the environment should be carefully assessed prior to any mining by this method.

Classification of Ore Deposits

Many attempts have been made to classify ore deposits. No single system is entirely satisfactory, yet each has some merit. Table 2–8 is a modified version of the classification first proposed by Waldemar Lindgren in 1913. Used with caution, it is still a convenient guide to various ore deposits. Estimates of temperature and pressure are subject to large uncertainties, so different types of deposits may overlap in many instances. This classification can be used for any ore introduced in the following chapters.

TABLE 2–8 The Lindgren ore deposit classification (modified).

I. Deposits dependent on chemical concentration processes under wide limits of temperature and pressure
A. Magmatic processes for deposits in igneous rocks
1. *Magmatic segregation (high temperature and pressure):* ore minerals segregated from rock-forming silicates by gravitational settling (i.e., sulfides; magnetite) or rising (i.e., ilmenite fixed on feldspar).
2. *Pegmatites (high to moderate temperatures, high pressures).*
B. Magmatic-related processes for deposits in rocks close to or intruded by igneous rocks
1. *Introduction of elements originating from the magma.*

TABLE 2–8 (continued)

(a) *Direct igneous interaction*
—Volcanic sublimates or fumaroles (temperatures variable 500–100°C; pressure atmospheric to low)
—Igneous metamorphic deposits; fluids from magma penetrate and are fixed in intruded rock

(b) *Hydrothermal (hot-water-rich) solutions containing igneous-derived chemicals*
—Hypothermal deposits (great depths; 300–500°C; high pressure)
—Mesothermal deposits (intermediate depths; 200–300°C; high pressure)
—Epithermal deposits (slight depths; 50–200°C; moderate pressure)
—Telethermal deposits (very shallow depths; temperature and pressure low)
—Xenothermal deposits (shallow depths but at high temperatures)

(c) *Origin not due to igneous activity*
—Deposits formed from circulating waters of unspecified origin temperatures usually less than 100°C; moderate pressure

2. *Concentrations in the rock bodies.*
   (a) Due to regional and dynamic metamorphism; temperature low to 400°C; high pressure
   (b) Deposits from deeply circulating groundwaters at temperatures to 100°C; moderate pressures
   (c) Deposits due to rock weathering and residual processes; low temperatures; pressures atmospheric to moderate

C. Deposits from surface waters

   1. *Solution interactions at temperatures to 70°C; moderate pressures.* Reactions may be inorganic, organic or both.
   2. *Solvent evaporation.*

II. Mechanical accumulations at moderate to low temperatures and pressures

SOURCE: Adapted from W. Lindgren, *Mineral Deposits* (New York: McGraw-Hill, 1933). Reprinted with permission.

Water: The Most Valuable Resource

Water is the world's most valuable resource. Agricultural industry, population growth and distribution, industrial expansion, and exploitation of mineral commodities are controlled by availability of water. For example, lunar samples returned by *Apollo II* astronauts in 1969 were examined for structurally bonded water in minerals as a source for water on the moon. Unfortunately, none was found and the lunar program was modified considerably.

Another example concerns exploitation of oil-marlstones located in remote and arid terrain. The potential carbon fuel and aluminum content of oil-marlstones (*shales*) is large. In the 1974 Workshop on Oil Shale Analysis sponsored by the National Science Foundation it was pointed out that roughly three barrels of water would be required for each barrel of crude oil recovered from oil shale. Developing new sources of water from wilderness areas or reallocating watershed supplies earmarked for agricultural and industrial purposes was not deemed feasible. In brief, the water supply is inadequate for successful exploitation of oil shales with present technology for kerogen removal and land reclamation. Let us consider the overall water picture in terms of the hydrologic cycle, worldwide distribution, and supply and demand in the United States.

The Hydrologic Cycle

An abbreviated view of the *hydrologic cycle* is shown in Figure 3–1. Circulation of water between the atmosphere, hydrosphere, and lithosphere is continuous. As Table 3–1 shows,

WATER: THE MOST VALUABLE RESOURCE

the oceans are the greatest reservoir of available water.* The amount that evaporates from the oceans to form clouds controls the quantity of water available to the continents. Solar energy and gravity, two main factors affecting water circulation, control the ever-changing weather patterns. Uneven water circulation was well illustrated during the 1976–77 winter months in the United States. A relatively slight shift in Arctic air masses subjected the eastern United States to extremely frigid conditions and record precipitation. The western United States, on the other hand, experienced relatively mild temperatures and extremely low total precipitation. This last factor led to near-drought conditions for the winter months and might have led to more local drought because snowpack in the watershed terrain was not replenished. Furthermore, because soil moisture was not replenished as in normal years, fire risk increased; with fires comes more rapid runoff of summer and fall rains, thus enhancing the drought conditions.

Although the last few statements are partly speculative, we see that yearly precipitation is variable and even the most technologically advanced nations cannot efficiently control it. As illustrated in Figure 3–1, the hydrologic cycle can be affected by abnormal evaporation, transpira-

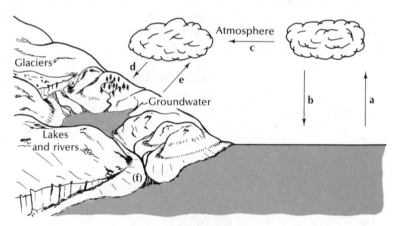

FIGURE 3–1 The hydrologic cycle. The reservoirs of water contain (in units of 10^{15} liters): atmosphere—12.9; oceans—1,318,160; glacial ice—29,100; lakes and rivers—231; and groundwaters—8384. The cycle is (a) ocean water loses 360×10^{15} liters per year to the atmosphere; (b) 323×10^{15} liters are returned by rainfall; (c) about 37×10^{15} liters are carried over the continents, where (d) evapotranspiration adds 62×10^{15} liters, while (e) 98×10^{15} liters fall to the continents as rain and snow; and (f) finally, 37×10^{15} liters return to the oceans by runoff, thus completing the cycle.

---

*Water content at great depths within the earth is unknown, although some water reaches surface reservoirs through extremely slow processes.

TABLE 3–1   The earth's water.

Type	Location	Volume (liters)	Percent of Total
Surface waters			
	Freshwater lakes	1.25×10^{17}	0.009
	Saline lakes; inland seas	1.04×10^{17}	0.008
	Stream channels	1.00×10^{15}	0.0001
Subsurface waters			
	Vadose water (water from water table to surface)	6.7×10^{16}	0.005
	Groundwater (to depth of 850 meters, or 0.5 mile)	4.17×10^{18}	0.31
	Deep groundwater (below depth of 850 meters, or 0.5 mile)	$4.17 \times 10^{18}(?)$	0.31
Other reservoirs			
	Icecaps and glaciers	2.9×10^{19}	2.15
	Atmosphere	1.3×10^{16}	0.001
	World's oceans	1.32×10^{21}	97.2

SOURCE: U.S. Geological Survey, Water Supply Papers, 1962.

tion, reservoir changes, and other factors. When we refer to water as a renewable resource, let us remember that the rate of local consumption can far outstrip the rate of renewal. In the early 1970s severe drought in the deserts of northern Africa caused mass starvation in Chad, Upper Volta, and parts of other countries. Inspection of the earth, especially by using LANDSAT photos, showed that vegetation loss from centuries of uncontrolled grazing caused the encroachment of desert into previously semiarid areas. Rapid runoff and evaporation of rainfall resulted. Governmental policies and controls—both of which are difficult to predict—may determine whether the situation can be improved.

Water Reservoirs

As shown in Table 3–1, the oceans contain about 97 percent of the available water in the hydrologic cycle. Yet due to its high dissolved salt content relatively little is consumed directly. Most water from the oceans is supplied to the continents by the combined processes of evaporation, cloud transport, precipitation, and storage.

WATER: THE MOST VALUABLE RESOURCE

Before returning to direct utilization of ocean waters, let us examine various reservoirs on the continents. Less than 0.02 percent of the water in the hydrosphere is contained in lakes, rivers, and stream channels, yet much of the water consumed is from these sources. While appealing at first glance, building large dams to increase storage is usually not wise. The overdamming of the Colorado River and its tributaries is a classic example. Arguments for local flood control, hydroelectric power generation, and additional water for consumption are all viable. However, the short-range effect of this overdamming is virtual cessation of agricultural activity near the Mexican border, and the United States has had to compensate the Mexican government for its water loss.

Dams also retain copious amounts of silt, thus limiting encroachments into downstream waters from headwaters of rivers and decreasing the amount of nutrients carried into preexisting floodplains. Unfortunately, because of silt, the amount of water stored is quite often less than anticipated before construction of the dam.

The Aswan Dam in Egypt is frequently cited as an example of poor planning. While flooding in the upper Nile has indeed been controlled, the once booming agricultural industry in the floodplain near the dam has been ruined. Furthermore, only part of the water impounded by the Aswan Dam can be used for hydroelectric power because greater power generation would demand more water than can be replenished. Finally, the eutrophication of the lake behind the Aswan Dam has increased at such a rapid rate that extensive water treatment is required for many uses. In short, very careful planning is required for water storage at any stage in the hydrologic cycle.

Vadose water (between the land surface and the water table) constitutes only 0.015 percent of the hydrosphere, and *groundwater* (to a depth of approximately 850 meters, or 0.5 mile) constitutes about 0.3 percent. These two sources are often easier to use than waters impounded by dams because the storage is natural and renewal of these reservoirs is more predictable. Deep groundwater (more than 0.5 mile deep) is difficult to estimate, and its renewal is even more difficult to evaluate. When deep wells are drilled, water removal must be carefully monitored because the *recharge* to deep-seated rocks is inadequately known. Any long-range venture to use groundwater on a continuous basis without some plan for artificial recharge would be a considerable gamble.

The atmosphere contains about 0.001 percent of the earth's water. This small part of the hydrosphere is extremely important because it controls the water supplied from the oceans to the continents. Because annual worldwide precipitation is rather monotonous but can fluctuate, people must plan water use accordingly. Cloud seeding can induce precipitation, but care must be taken not to drastically alter watershed conditions by overseeding. Continued cloud seeding requires a regular supply of evaporated water from the oceans in specific areas; but irregular supply is the rule, not the exception. We should not consider cloud seeding except in times of two- to four-year periods of below-normal annual precipitation. For example, such a seeding project was approved for northern California in June 1977 as a stopgap measure due to the severe situation at that time.

Only 30 percent of total precipitation in the United States becomes streamflow; and only about 27 percent of that (i.e., 8 percent of total precipitation) is withdrawn for industrial, agricultural, and urban uses.* This relationship is presented in Figure 3–2. A staggering 73 percent of the streamflow is not recovered. Water withdrawn from streams must reach about 50 percent by 1980 and 80 percent by the year 2000[†], which will require careful planning. We have already seen that a large number of dams may not be the answer; and even water recycling only partly satisfies water quality requirements.

Of the precipitation that does not become streamflow, about 56 percent (i.e., 41 percent of the total) is contained in forests, pastures, and crop vegetation subject to the processes of evaporation and transpiration. The remaining 44 percent (31 percent of total precipitation) is lost through various mechanisms. Contour plowing techniques to impound water near urban areas are constantly being improved; the problem of impounding—and successfully using—precipitation in areas of dense population has not yet been solved.

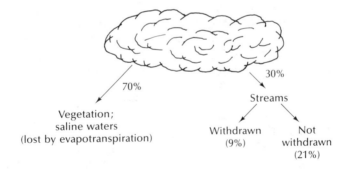

FIGURE 3–2 Precipitation in the United States. Only 9 percent of the total precipitation that falls on the United States is withdrawn for use. It is used for irrigation, industry, and municipalities. It has been estimated (see text) that we must find ways to use up to 80 percent of the water which accumulates in streams and lakes (about a threefold increase). Because there is no easy way to do this, water resources to serve our expanding population will remain one of our key problems.

---

*A. Wolman, Water Resources Publication 1000–B (Washington, D.C.: National Research Council–National Academy of Sciences, 1962).
     [†]Ibid.

Water in polar ice has long been an enticing potential resource. Indeed, polar ice contains more than 2 percent of the earth's water. However, methods for using this vast freshwater resource are still in the theoretical stage. The simplest way may be to tow small ice masses to a point where they will be carried by natural forces to desired latitudes and to anchor them close to major cities. While this does not seem practical now, it may become a reality in the twenty-first century.

Desalination

Water consumption in the United States has increased so rapidly that even the high estimates previously made may be obsolete. Between 1900 and 1970 U.S. water consumption increased from about 40 billion gallons to 355 billion gallons (150 to 1340 billion liters)*—nearly a ninefold increase. More alarming is that this increase is not linear; consumption is increasing at a faster rate than is population growth. Coping with this problem will require more ways of trapping and storing precipitated water and finding ways to use the ocean waters as well.

Desalination, the removal of dissolved salts from saline waters, can be accomplished in many ways, but none are economic on a worldwide scale. Small desalination plants have been designed for sea-going vessels. There are also methods for desalinating sea water, saline lake water, and brackish water. Methods involving evaporation and rapid condensation work relatively well in areas where the sea water is very warm. For example, Israel uses desalinated water for much of its agricultural needs. Other countries in the Mideast are developing desalination plants, especially where initial costs are of little concern, as in the OPEC nations. Frozen ocean water contains very little dissolved salts; and methods for rapidly freezing ocean water to produce fresh water are in use in Ipswich, England, and other places. Unfortunately, the freezing method is too expensive and the waters not quite cold enough to make this technology practical for cities in the northeastern United States. Desalination plants are used extensively in the Caribbean Islands—not because of a technological breakthrough or ideal waters, but because continued tourism supports plants that would be uneconomic elsewhere. There is a message there as well: If economics control desalination, then increased funding for research to reduce costs seems essential in this crucial area. The Saline Water Act of 1952 provided $2 million for research in desalination over a five-year period; and $2 billion was made available for the period 1965–72. Because this research led to several breakthroughs, even use of continental saline waters now appears realistic although other economic factors (such as supplies and labor) outweigh the "funding

*U.S. Geological Survey, Water Supply Papers, 1960–70.

aspects." At present, it is estimated that more than thirty countries have possibilities for economic desalination of sea water.*

As research in solar and nuclear energy is conducted, ways of using the sun and fission energy for desalination are being contemplated. Should either approach prove to be successful in coastal areas, then it would be logical to use it for desalination of inland brackish waters.

Use of Water in the United States

In the United States water is used mainly for irrigation and industrial purposes; about 415,000 million liters for each purpose are withdrawn every day. Public and rural withdrawals are 64,400 million and 11,400 million liters per day respectively. Of the 415,000 million liters per day used for irrigation, about 25 percent is lost due to evaporation or seepage into the ground. Thus approximately 92 percent of all U.S. water consumption is for industry and agriculture; and only 7 percent is used for public water supplies. At first glance this would indicate an adequate water supply. However, as pointed out earlier in this chapter, even slight variations in total annual precipitation can cause local excesses or near-drought conditions. Furthermore, some 60 percent of the water used for irrigation is consumed by plants or lost by evaporation. Much of the water used by industry and the public is not consumed, but it may be polluted so that immediate reuse is not possible. The relative importance of water can be appreciated by considering the various flows into and out of a hypothetical city of one million people, as shown in Table 3–2.

TABLE 3–2   Inflows and outflows for a hypothetical city of one million people.

	Kilograms/day (thousands)	Tons/ day
Inflows:		
Water	567,000	625,000
Food, coal, oil, gas, and fuel	9,525	10,500
Outflows:		
Sewage	226,800	500,000
Refuse	1,815	2,000
Particles	135	150
Sulfur and nitrogen oxides	225	250
Hydrocarbons and carbon monoxide	500	550

SOURCE: Modified from A. Wolman, "Metabolism of Cities," *Scientific American* 213 (1965): 30. Reprinted by permission.

*United Nations, *Water Desalination in Developing Countries*, 1976.

WATER: THE MOST VALUABLE RESOURCE

Runoff water in streams and rivers provides only 20 percent of the water used by municipalities; the remaining 80 percent comes from wells. Careful planning is necessary to maintain an adequate water supply. For example, in Albuquerque, New Mexico, a large part of the water consumed is supplied from wells. Most of these wells are located near the Rio Grande, and prior to 1975 there was an ample supply of water. In 1975 the Cochiti Dam north of Albuquerque was completed to impound water and to control flooding. Although the dam has been successful for both purposes, its discharge of water has not been as high as the pre-1975 river flow and has decreased the rate of *flushing* on the Rio Grande south of the dam. This has also lowered the water table in the area of highest water well density, requiring the drilling of additional new wells and causing some older wells to be abandoned. While the pre-1975 flow was adequate to remove much of the sewage discharged into the Rio Grande, the decreased river flow has led to more pollution at the depth where well water was routinely recovered. This has led to abandonment of some wells, drilling of new deeper wells, and additional costs for sewage treatment.

The forty-eight coterminous states are divided into eighteen regions for the purpose of discussing water supply and demand,[*] because water is very unevenly distributed throughout the United States. Figure 3–3 shows the eighteen regions and the 1970 figures for water withdrawn from runoff for use (first number) and water consumed (second number). Despite the apparently favorable ratio of water withdrawn to water consumed, the amount withdrawn in some areas may actually be only one-third that shown in Figure 3–3. This is due to extreme seasonal fluctuations in many areas. When potential assured supply (PAS) is compared with projected commitments (PC) for these same eighteen regions, only in three regions is the ratio PAS/PC much greater than one. In seven other regions this ratio is about one, but may be slightly greater or less than one as a function of seasonal rainfall, new commitments, dams, and other factors. In the remaining eight regions the PAS/PC is less than one.[†]

How we arrive at the data in Figure 3–3 is critical. For the southwestern United States the amount of water withdrawn would not meet consumption demands were it not for dams and other means of diverting water into this region. The region's supply is augmented by inflow of water from the Upper Colorado region, importation of surface water, and mining of groundwater.[**] Now, however, increased water demand in this area because of mineral exploration and development (oil shales and others), increased agricultural and urban demands, and industrial growth will require even more from the Upper Colorado region;

---

[*] I. C. James II, J. C. Kammerer, and C. R. Murray, "How Much Water in a 12-ounce Can?" U.S. Geological Survey Annual Report, 1976.

[†] Wolman, op. cit.

[**] C. R. Murray and E. B. Reeves, "Estimated Water Use in the United States in 1970," U.S. Geological Survey Circular 676, 1979.

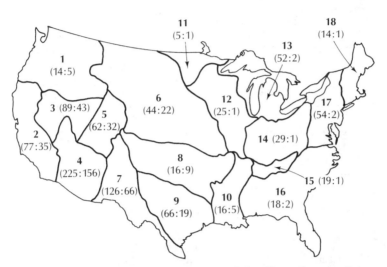

FIGURE 3–3 Water resource regions of the 48 contiguous states: **1.** Columbia–North Pacific; **2.** California–South Pacific; **3.** Great Basin; **4.** Lower Colorado; **5.** Upper Colorado; **6.** Missouri; **7.** Rio Grande; **8.** Arkansas-White-Red; **9.** Texas-Gulf; **10.** Lower Mississippi; **11.** Souris-Red-Rainy; **12.** Upper Mississippi; **13.** Great Lakes; **14.** Ohio; **15.** Tennessee; **16.** South Atlantic–Gulf; **17.** Middle Atlantic; and **18.** New England. The first number in parentheses is the percentage of average runoff withdrawn for 1970; the second number is the percentage of average runoff consumed in 1970. These figures can exceed 100% in areas where rainfall is low and water is removed from dams. Furthermore, the first figure may be high by a factor of 3 in areas receiving relatively little total precipitation, as in the arid Southwest. (From C. R. Murray and E. B. Reeves, "Estimated Use of Water in the United States in 1970," U.S. Geological Survey Circular 676, 1972.)

and the amount available may not be sufficient to meet demand by the year 2000.

Table 3–3 presents data for water withdrawn and consumed for the United States. More water is withdrawn than is consumed because it is used mostly for industry, irrigation, and other nonconsumptive purposes.

Water Conservation

The conservation of water is a worldwide problem; yet despite attempts to educate consumers, conservation efforts are moving very slowly in most countries. Although an individual needs somewhat less than 2 liters

TABLE 3–3 Water withdrawn and consumed by region for the United States.

Region	Area (thousands of km²)	Stream Discharge (hm³/day)	Population (millions) 1970	Withdrawals (hm³/day) 1970	Water Consumption (hm³/day) 1970
31 eastern states (8 eastern regions)	2713	2800	144.7	770	45
10 central states (5 central regions)	2980	640	27.1	240	110
7 western states (5 western regions)	2132	1100	30.3	370	170
48 states	7825	4500	202	1400	320

per day to survive, in the United States actual household use may range from about 40 liters per day in homes without plumbing to well over several hundred liters per day for homes with large plumbing systems, large lawns, and the like. The largest household uses of water are for the flushing of toilets and watering of lawns, with bathing also contributing considerably.* These and other data are shown in Table 3–4.

TABLE 3–4 Domestic use of water by a family of four.

Family Use	Liters/day per Family	Liters/day per Capita
Drinking and kitchen uses	30	7.6
Dishwasher (3 loads/day)	57	14
Toilet (16 flushes/day)	363	91
Bathing (4 baths or showers/day)	303	76
Laundering (6 loads/week)	129	32
Auto washing (twice per month)	38	9.5
Lawn watering (180 hours/year)	379	95
Garbage disposal (1% of other uses)	13	3
Total	1312	328

SOURCE: James et al., op. cit.

*James et al., op. cit.

Home conservation—whether voluntary or mandatory—is not the answer, however. Table 3–5 shows the U.S. national averages for per capita freshwater use in 1970. Although every effort to conserve should and must be made, these data clearly show that the greatest amount of fresh water can be saved in nondomestic consumption. While many methods of domestic saving are possible (i.e., the total amount of water used directly or indirectly for producing a 12-ounce can is 63 liters!), measures such as recycling water for industrial and other purposes will have a far greater effect on conservation.

Future water use is expected to outweigh supplies. Some major contributing factors include strip mining of coal and possible oil-marlstone mining (most of which will occur in the semiarid West); conversion of coal to alternate energy forms such as liquid fuels; electricity for transportation; and the development of secondary industries and urban growth. Careful planning for these areas will be necessary to maintain our water supplies, and we must make every effort to develop water-efficient operations and strategies for on-site and off-site conservation. If these measures are not taken, then the United States will indeed face severe water supply problems in the twenty-first century.

TABLE 3–5 Estimated daily per capita use of fresh water in the United States (1970 national averages).

Water Use	Liters/Person/Day
Domestic (indoor and outdoor uses; home connected to public water supply)	280
Public water systems (fire-fighting, parks, etc., for 166 million people)	628
Self-supplied industrial use (for 206 million people)	2,940
All irrigation (excluding hydroelectric power)	5,870
Hydroelectric power	51,500

SOURCE: James et al., op. cit.

Metals

Abundant Metals

Elements having *metallic properties* such as ductility, high thermal conductivity, malleability, high electrical conductivity, and strength are classified as *metals*. Some elements classified as metals (e.g., magnesium and titanium) are also used as compounds and are included here following conventional listings in other works. The abundant metals include iron, aluminum, magnesium, and titanium.

Iron

Iron is the fourth most abundant element in the earth's crust (by weight) and, more importantly, the industrial foundation of most nations. The iron industry accounts for over 90 percent of all metals mined and also contributes to the production of iron alloys.

Most iron production is from *Precambrian** banded-iron formations. Principal iron minerals are *magnetite, hematite,* and *goethite* (Table 4–1). All six major continents contain abundant reserves of iron; and world trade in iron is highly competitive. The United States, while possessing adequate reserves and resources to meet its needs for many decades, still imports roughly 30 percent of the 130 million tons it consumes each year. There are diverse reasons for the large amount of imports. One important reason is importing helps to maintain a favorable trade relationship with countries which also provide commodities that are scarce in the United States. Thus iron and nickel are imported from Canada, iron ore and manganese from Brazil, and iron ore and titanium ore from Australia. Furthermore, by maintaining a steady stream

*Precambrian refers to that segment of earth history between roughly 570 million years ago and the earth's formation some 4600 million years ago.

of imports the U.S. domestic reserves are preserved. It is essential to maintain a stable price base for iron (and steel) because even slight price fluctuations affect tremendous tonnages. In addition, the production of many other metals is dependent on the iron industry.

Many metals are being used as substitutes for iron (especially aluminum), but the effect on iron consumption is slight. Every highly industrialized nation depends on iron. There is a direct correlation between iron consumption and standard of living in these nations.

Most of the U.S. iron reserves and resources are located in the Precambrian banded-rocks of the Lake Superior region. Most of the ore is low grade and requires enrichment by beneficiation and agglomeration prior to smelting in blast furnaces.

Iron ore deposits fall into four main types:

1. *Precambrian bedded iron deposits* which dwarf the Phanerozoic* bedded ironstones and bog iron or clastic deposits.

2. Ore associated with igneous processes by *magmatic segregation* such as the magnetite-bearing igneous rocks of the Kiruna, Sweden, area and magnetite in contact metamorphic zones (e.g., the now mined-out Cornwall, Pennsylvania, deposit is a classic example).

3. *Hydrothermal deposits* not associated directly with magmatic processes.

4. *Near-surface* or *surface deposits,* including iron laterites and low-grade deposits enriched by weathering and related processes.

The Precambrian bedded iron deposits are so important that they deserve some special attention here. Typically, these deposits contain from 20 to 45 percent iron deposited by sedimentary processes and interlayered with chert, carbonates, and other silicates. Where these deposits have been metamorphosed, the original mineral assemblages have been changed but not the basic iron content. These deposits are low in aluminum, sodium, potassium, and other minor elements, thus making the metallurgical extraction of iron relatively simple. The Precambrian bedded iron deposits were probably formed at a time when the oxygen content of the atmosphere was so low that most ionic iron was present as Fe^{2+}, between about 3 billion and 2 billion years ago. By about 1.8 billion to 1.7 billion years ago the oxygen content of the atmosphere had increased such that Fe^{3+} became important in surface or near-surface processes; extensive bedded iron deposits are not found in rocks formed after this period.

Phanerozoic refers to earth history between the present and 570 million years ago.

Some of the Precambrian bedded iron deposits contain only about 15 percent iron; the taconites of the Lake Superior region are good examples. The potential of this resource was not tapped until ways were found to *beneficiate* the ore so that iron could be profitably extracted. In brief, *beneficiation* uses the magnetic properties and high density of iron to separate the iron-rich parts of the taconite ore from the gangue during initial crushing and premilling treatment. Taconite ore now accounts for

TABLE 4–1 Abundant metals.

Minerals	Formula	Remarks or Occurrence
IRON		
Magnetite	Fe_3O_4	Igneous rocks
Hematite	Fe_2O_3	Sedimentary or residual deposits
Goethite (Limonite)	$FeO(OH)$	Sedimentary or residual deposits
Siderite	$FeCO_3$	Sedimentary rocks
Iron silicates	Variable	Banded sedimentary rocks (including taconite)
ALUMINUM		
Gibbsite	$Al(OH)_3$	Main mineral in bauxite (aluminum laterite) ore
Diaspore	$AlO(OH)$	Residual ore
Nepheline*	$NaAl SiO_4$	Igneous rocks
Kaolinite[†]	$Al_2Si_2O_5(OH)_4$	Sedimentary rocks and residual deposits
Aluminum-silicates[†] (kyanite, andalusite, sillimanite)	Al_2SiO_5	Metamorphic rocks
Dawsonite[†]	$NaAl(CO_3)(OH)_2$	In oil shale (marlstones)
MAGNESIUM		
Mg^{2+}	—	Recovery from sea water
Magnesite	$MgCO_3$	Veins in metamorphic or carbonate-rich rocks
Dolomite	$CaMg(CO_3)_2$	Sedimentary rocks
TITANIUM		
Ilmenite	$FeTiO_3$	Igneous rocks or placers
Rutile	TiO_2	Igneous or metamorphic rocks; placers

*Used as aluminum ore when rock is mined for several purposes.
[†]Future ores: (i) kaolinite—when technology advances to point where aluminum can be profitably extracted; (ii) aluminum silicates—when ways to concentrate minerals are found; and (iii) dawsonite will be abundant when oil shales are mined.

more than 60 percent of the total iron ore produced in the United States, according to the U.S. Bureau of Mines.

Many of the iron-bearing formations are folded and the dips of the beds are very steep. Iron deposits in the Lake Superior region, the Labrador deposits, and Hammersley Range (Australia) deposits fall into this category. Mining of rocks so folded allows for relatively simple planning, as illustrated in Figure 4–1. Because the iron content is so uniform, open pits are planned to a specific depth below which recovery is uneconomic. When this is cut-off depth is reached in one open pit mine, equipment is moved to another mine which is not yet so deep. Mining ores in this fashion is likely to continue in Labrador and elsewhere. There is a question however, whether some of the waste silicate gangue dumped into Lake Superior may contain carcinogenic minerals. The importance of iron ore production from the Lake Superior region is shown in Figure 4–2.

Early attempts to extract iron from ore led to the production of wrought iron and pig iron as higher temperatures were achieved. The development of modern blast furnaces has finally allowed highly efficient recovery of iron. The ore is mixed in the blast furnace with native carbon (in the form of high-grade coking coal) and with limestone. Coal acts as a reductant for the oxidized iron. Molten native iron is formed, carbon-oxidized, and removed as carbon dioxide (CO_2). Limestone acts as a flux to remove impurities in the iron ore. For the production of one ton

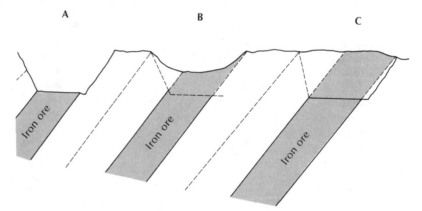

FIGURE 4–1 Banded iron-ore deposits. Many of the world's iron ore deposits occur in uniform, banded metamorphosed sedimentary rocks and are commonly tilted as shown. Open pit mining methods are effective because the ore is near the surface and low in grade. Ideally, as open pit **A** is completed, **B** is very nearly ready, and **C** will begin producing when **A** has been shut down and **B** is half-finished. It is cheaper to develop pits **B** and **C** to the same depth as **A** rather than to deepen **A**. This type of mining is common for the extensive iron ores in Labrador.

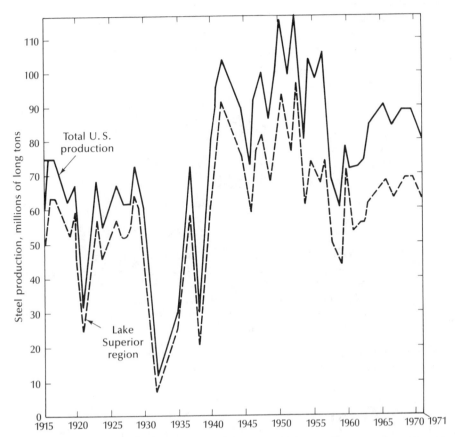

FIGURE 4–2 Importance of domestic iron ore reserves. Although U.S. reserves and resources are abundant, about 33 percent of the iron ore treated in this country is imported. This results from not wishing to use domestic reserves too rapidly and to stabilize our balance of trade with countries with excess iron ore.

(900 kilograms) of cast iron* from ore containing 55 to 70 percent iron, about 550 pounds (250 kilograms) of limestone and 1100 pounds (500 kilograms) of coke are needed. Cast iron is tempered into steel by additional blasting and adding carbon at very high temperatures. A sketch of a blast furnace for steel production is shown in Figure 4–3.

Coke for the iron-smelting process is most easily produced from anthracite; and there is doubt about future availability of anthracite for the iron industry even though iron resources are plentiful. If coal is the answer to our energy needs, then ways must be developed to use

*Also named pig iron, after the shape of the containers into which the molten iron was poured.

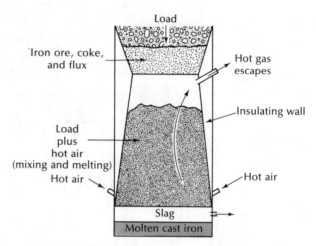

FIGURE 4–3 Blast furnace for cast iron. Low-grade iron ore is crushed, mixed with clay, and rolled to get iron-ore enriched pellets that can be separated by magnetic means. The other essential ingredients—limestone flux and coking coal—are combined with the iron pellets before hot air is added. Slag is driven off, and molten cast iron remains.

lower grades of coal for energy production and save the anthracite for the steel industry.

Aluminum

Aluminum is the third most abundant element by weight in the earth's crust, yet most of it is bonded to oxygen in silicates and is extremely difficult to extract. Consequently, little of the world's aluminum is produced from the most common rock-forming minerals, the *aluminosilicate feldspars*.

Only iron surpasses aluminum in use as a metal; and uses for aluminum continue to increase. As a lightweight yet strong metal, aluminum is ideal for construction materials and transportation vehicles. Other well-known uses include beverage cans (many of which are being recycled), electrical equipment, and military equipment.

The United States consumed about four million tons of aluminum metal in 1970—about one-third of world consumption according to the U.S. Bureau of Mines. Most aluminum consumed in the United States is produced domestically, although we rely heavily on imports of aluminum ore (Figure 4–4). Prior to the mid-nineteenth century, rare minerals such as cryolite (Na_3AlF_6) were used because the aluminum could be extracted with existing technology. At the time aluminum was not considered to be a useful iron substitute. Although *bauxite* was discov-

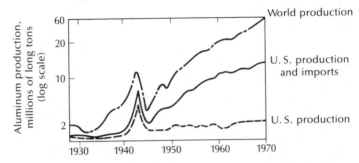

FIGURE 4–4 Aluminum production. Aluminum production was severely limited before 1930 because it was difficult to extract the metal from rocks. When methods were developed in 1935 to treat bauxite ores, aluminum production jumped. At present, U.S. ore is too expensive to mine, so we rely on imports for about 80 percent of our needs (which is about one-third of world consumption). Aluminum metal extraction uses about 4 percent of our total electrical energy.

ered in the 1800s, aluminum production remained at a low level until technological advances made aluminum extraction profitable. The importance of aluminum was fully recognized with the coming of World War II and since then the industry has continued to thrive.

The principal ore of aluminum is bauxite. Bauxite, more properly called an aluminum laterite, is formed under tropical weathering conditions, where aluminum-rich source rocks are exposed to very intense and prolonged rainfall and rainfall exceeds water loss by evaporation (Figure 4–5). Under these conditions, and presuming the rocks exposed are in a geologically stable area, most of the common rock-forming elements such as sodium, potassium, magnesium, calcium, and silicon are removed by weathering. Aluminum remains as gibbsite, $Al(OH)_3$, which is the principal mineral of bauxite ore, plus diaspore and boehmite. Aluminum is relatively insoluble in natural solutions and can be successfully separated from silica in regions of tropical weathering.

Better ways of recovering aluminum from ore became necessary with the discovery of and need for more bauxite. Unlike silicates (where aluminum substitutes for silicon and both are tightly bonded to oxygen), aluminum in bauxite ore is less strongly bonded to oxygen. It can be recovered by the Bayer process, in which the ore is leached under pressure and at high temperature in the presence of a basic, sodium-rich solution. The resulting product is soluble sodium aluminate, and most impurities remain behind as solids. Hydrated aluminum oxide is then precipitated, and aluminum metal is produced from it by electrolysis. This is not a cheap process; roughly three percent of the annual electrical energy consumption in the United States is for aluminum-metal production.

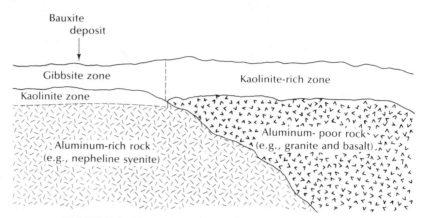

Bauxite
deposit

Gibbsite zone

Kaolinite zone

Kaolinite-rich zone

Aluminum-rich rock
(e.g., nepheline syenite)

Aluminum- poor rock
(e.g., granite and basalt)

FIGURE 4–5 Formation of bauxite. Bauxite forms under conditions of tropical weathering. Some aluminous rocks such as nepheline syenite are severely weathered until only aluminum-rich minerals such as gibbsite are left. Nepheline syenites are ideal for bauxite (i.e., aluminum laterites) to develop because they contain a high ratio of aluminum to silicon. In rocks such as basalt and granite, the clay mineral kaolinite will develop easily during weathering, but there is too much silicon present for it to be completely removed. Hence gibbsite, the main mineral of bauxites, will not form.

Critical to formation of bauxite deposits is presence of an aluminum-rich source rock. Nepheline syenites (and equivalent aluminum-rich and silica-impoverished igneous rocks) are common as source materials. These rocks are actively sought in present-day tropical regions and, based on precontinental drift reconstruction, older tropical environments as well. When more silicic igneous rocks (i.e., granite through granodiorite) are exposed to the same tropical conditions, the end product is usually kaolinite-rich deposits from which only part of the silica has been removed. Thus while a typical bauxite formed from syenite may contain roughly 40 percent aluminum, the clay-mineral kaolinite contains only about 21 percent. Kaolinite and other nonclay aluminum silicates will remain uneconomic as aluminum ores until better technology is developed.

Bauxites commonly form from argillaceous limestones that have been exposed to tropical weathering (Figure 4–6). The carbonate fraction is readily dissolved, leaving behind a beneficiated, aluminum-rich clay accumulation from which bauxites develop. Unlike the hypothetical weathering of silica-rich rocks like granite to form kaolinite, the aluminum-rich clays formed by weathering of limestones is apparently so pronounced and rapid that bauxites form from the aluminum-clay-rich residuum of the limestone.

Dawsonite ($NaAl(OH)_2CO_3$) in oil-marlstones contains aluminum that can easily be extracted because it is readily soluble. As oil-

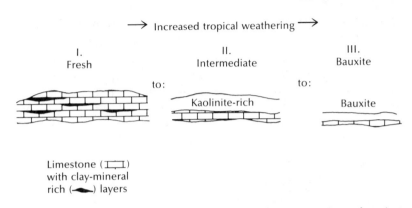

Limestone (⊏⊐)
with clay-mineral
rich (━━) layers

FIGURE 4–6 Formation of bauxite from limestone. Some bauxites form from rocks which contain relatively aluminum-rich layers. Most limestones are impure, and the clay minerals they contain are typically aluminum-rich. When exposed to tropical weathering, the limestone itself is readily removed and kaolinite is formed or concentrated from pre-existing clay minerals. Further weathering results in the formation of bauxite deposits as shown. This is typical of the deposits in the Caribbean Islands.

marlstones are developed, aluminum from dawsonite will be recovered as a by-product. The advantage of using low-grade dawsonite ore is that it dissolves to form sodium aluminate, thus eliminating the necessity for Bayer process.

Bauxite, it was stated, is actually aluminum-rich laterite. If iron or nickel remain (e.g., due to different parent materials), then iron laterites or nickel laterites will form. The latter are used for nickel ores in several parts of the world.

Magnesium

Magnesium is the eighth most abundant element by weight in the earth's crust. It is used as an oxide for refractory applications, as the carbonate for many chemicals, and for light corrosion-resistant alloys. Methods for magnesium recovery from sea water started in 1940 have proven so successful that there is virtually an inexhaustible supply of the metal. However, commercial deposits of magnesium compounds such as magnesite, dolomite, and brucite are widespread throughout the world. They are mined primarily for use in the chemical industry. Because magnesium is not as useful as aluminum as a light metal, U.S. and world consumption will not rival that of iron and aluminum. The United States has an abundance of magnesium, as shown in annual exports of 122,000 short tons (110,700 metric tons) of magnesium compounds compared with imports of only 5200 short tons (4720 metric tons) of scrap magnesium alloys and other materials.*

Deposits of magnesite and dolomite, as well as potential magnesium chloride (Mg Cl$_2$) from saline lakes, are widespread in the United States. Magnesite deposits are commonly associated with ultra-mafic rocks, whereas dolomite occurs more often in dolomite-rich limestone. (If sufficiently rich in dolomite, the rocks are referred to as dolostones.)

Titanium

Titanium (Ti) is the only mineral resource listed as a metal, yet it is used mainly in the chemical industry as a paint pigment. However, its increasing use in the aerospace industry for its metallic properties warrants its inclusion here. The U.S. government lists titanium as a strategic commodity and stockpiles it accordingly. Data for titanium are shown in Figure 4–7.

Titanium is widespread as an accessory element in many rock-forming minerals (e.g., amphiboles and pyroxenes); but fortunately, it is also the major cation in rock-forming accessory minerals such as rutile (TiO$_2$) and ilmenite (FeTiO$_3$). It is from these accessory minerals that most production of titanium results. Special ultramafic rocks such as anorthosites commonly contain enormous amounts of ilmenite, concentrated by magmatic segregation. Lesser amounts of both ilmenite and rutile are associated with mafic and ultramafic rocks. While direct extraction of the latter is difficult, these rocks weather fairly easily, and the titanium minerals resistant to weathering are concentrated in placers or beach sands. At present, due to abundant world supply, the only titanium recovered in the United States is from beach sands off the coast of Florida. Most of the rutile used in the United States is imported from Australia; and the United States ranks behind Norway and Australia in ilmenite production. Despite our stockpiling of titanium, the United States still was able to increase 1974 exports by 46 percent over 1973 exports.[†] A description of ore minerals for the abundant metals and where they occur is given in Table 4–1.

The Less Abundant and Scarce Metals

Manganese is listed in some texts as an abundant metal, the twelfth most abundant by weight in the earth's crust. In this book we will consider it one of the less abundant metals.

*U.S. Bureau of Mines, *Minerals Yearbook*, 1974.
[†] Ibid.

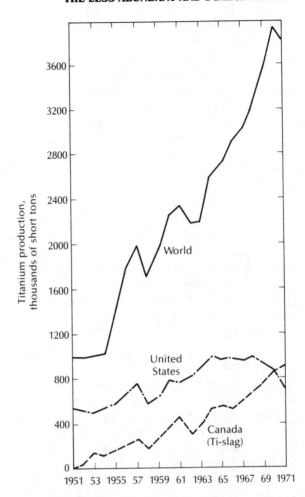

FIGURE 4–7 Titanium production. The titanium-bearing mineral ilmenite ($FeTiO_3$) is abundant in many mafic rocks. It is concentrated in rocks such as anorthosites and, due to its resistance to weathering, in placer deposits as well. As the U.S. production curve indicates, it is cheaper to import much of our ilmenite from Canada rather than mine some of our low-grade (but extensive) deposits.

Manganese presents some problems for the United States. The world supply is copious, but the last operating U.S. mine closed in 1972. Since then U.S. needs have been met by imports. More than 90 percent of manganese consumption in the United States is in the steel industry, where it is used as a raw additive to scavenge sulfur and oxygen (which are then channeled to the slag) and as an alloy. It is also used to a lesser extent as an oxidant in uranium milling and for other purposes by the chemical industry. Unfortunately, there is currently no adequate substitute for manganese as a scavenger in the steel industry, and imports continue to escalate. From 1973 to 1974 manganese imports increased by more than 8 percent.

There are extensive manganese deposits in the Western Hemisphere (primarily in Brazil, from whom the United States imports most of its manganese), although most is located elsewhere. In addition to Brazil, the United States imports from Gabon, the Republic of South Africa, Zaire, and Ghana. Due to political uncertainties, only Ghana can be counted as a continued source for manganese, and an extensive search is being conducted from Mexico southward for more manganese in the Western Hemisphere. For every ton of steel produced, some 15 to 20 pounds (7 to 9 kilograms) of manganese are needed, which illustrates the importance of manganese.

Because it is not abundant in the earth's crust, manganese must be concentrated many times before an ore deposit results. Typical ore contains from 25 to 50 percent manganese and is usually the result of sedimentary accumulations or rhodochrosite ($MnCO_3$) or pyrolusite (MnO_2). The ultimate source of the manganese in these deposits was undoubtedly Mn^{2+}, which substituted for Fe^{2+}. Manganese is locally enriched in eugeosynclinal sediments in island arc systems, but these deposits are minor compared with the other sedimentary types.

Of special interest are *manganese nodules* that cover wide areas of the ocean floors. Although the nodules are extremely impure, they are enriched in iron, copper, cobalt, chromium, and nickel, with lesser amounts of gold and other elements. Economic recovery of these nodules, which cover up to 2600 square kilometers in places,* is not yet possible, but industries and agencies pursuing this matter are optimistic. If recovery of manganese nodules should prove economic, then reliance on imports for manganese, chromium, nickel, and cobalt will be lessened.

Scarce Metals Concentrated as Sulfides

Many scarce metals are mined from deposits of sulfides. Others occur as oxides, and some metals occur as the native element. In this section we will consider the metals copper, lead, zinc, nickel, cobalt, molybdenum, and mercury—all of which are primarily concentrated in sulfides of the metal.

Copper   Copper mining is perhaps the best known. World copper reserves and resources will apparently be abundant for many years. Copper is occasionally concentrated as the native element (e.g., in Michigan), but

---

*U.S. Geological Survey, Professional Paper 820, 1973.

this is rare. Most of the world's copper comes from fractured porphyritic rocks in which copper mineralization has occurred. These porphyry-copper deposits contain very low-grade ore and must be mined by open-pit methods. Furthermore, they occur in well-recognized belts in several parts of the world (Figure 4–8) as classic examples of metallogenic provinces. More than 50 percent of the world's copper production is from porphyry-copper deposits, in spite of the ore's low grade. The mining of porphyry coppers is, in a sense, a test of patience and fortitude. Prior to open-pit mining (which commenced at the Bingham Canyon Mine, Utah, at the turn of the twentieth century), copper had been mined from high-grade but small vein deposits and from sedimentary deposits. Successful mining of low-grade ore (under 2 percent copper) led to exploration, discovery, and exploitation of the porphyry copper metallogenic provinces now recognized.

Copper's uses are many. Most is consumed for electrical applications (55 percent) and the remainder for construction, industrial machinery, the transportation industry, and chemical uses. Because copper is so ideally suited for electrical applications (i.e., excellent electrical and thermal conductivity, high strength, good malleability and ductility, and lack of magnetism) and is so widespread, the long-range future of the copper industry seems very favorable. Competition is extreme, however, with some sixty-five countries producing copper and eight (the United States, Chile, Canada, Zambia, USSR, Zaire, Peru, and the Philippines, in order of production) accounting for more than half the world production.

In porphyry coppers and in many other sulfide deposits the main copper-bearing mineral is chalcopyrite ($CuFeS_2$), with lesser amounts of enargite (Cu_3AsS_4), bornite ($CuFeS_4$), chalcocite (Cu_2S), and copper-bearing pyrite ((Fe, Cu)S_2). Because the rock is usually highly fractured, it can be excavated, crushed, and the sulfides concentrated from silicate and other gangue with relative ease. Copper is then recovered by electrolytic means.

Prospecting for copper is sometimes made easier by the bright green or blue minerals such as malachite and azurite (both basic copper carbonates) that are formed from sulfides by surface oxidation. These minerals allow prospectors to study other alteration effects and trace elements and to conduct a thorough search for possible subsurface sulfide deposits.

Twenty percent of the world's copper occurs in stratiform sedimentary deposits. The most famous of these is the Kupferschiefer-type deposits found in north central Europe. A thin bed of copper-sulfide–rich material was deposited over this area during the Permian period.* Although production has virtually ceased from the Kupfer-

---

*The Permian period is that span of earth history from about 225 to 270 million years before the present.

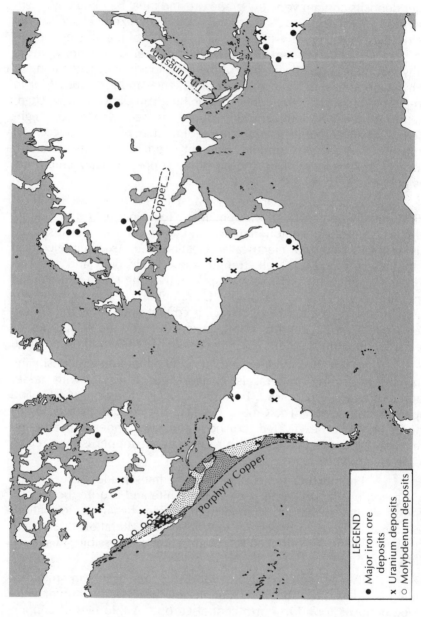

FIGURE 4–8 Worldwide metal ore distribution. The porphyry copper, molybdenum, and tin-tungsten belts are spatially associated with igneous rocks and major subduction zones. Iron and uranium do not show any regularity in their spatial relationship to orogenic belts or igneous rocks. Most of the iron

PLATE 9

Leached capping zone (dark-colored rock) and oxidized rocks (light colored) over porphyry copper at Cananea mine in Sonora, Mexico. (Courtesy of W.E. Elston.)

PLATE 10

Dump material from the Santa Rita porphyry copper mining operations in New Mexico. Although not shown in its entirety, the dump is so large that it is visible from some satellite views of the earth. (Courtesy of W. E. Elston.)

PLATE 11

Part of the Chino Pit, a porphyry copper deposit in Santa Rita, New Mexico. The entire pit is over one mile (1.7 kilometers) wide and 1500 feet (450 meters) deep. (Courtesy of W. E. Elston.)

schiefer deposits, recognition of this type of deposit led to the discovery of the sedimentary Zambia-Zaire copper belt (formed in a somewhat similar fashion) which dominates Africa's copper production. There are some questions about formation of sedimentary deposits of many metals; for example, was the metal deposited by sedimentary processes, enriched by sedimentary processes, enriched by secondary processes, or due to unexposed (metamorphic-derived) sources? These questions have not been resolved, but even partial answers will assist in future exploration.

About 30 percent of the world's copper comes from deposits smaller than the porphyry coppers. These include the vein deposits where massive sulfides fill fractured rocks, commonly near an igneous body (e.g., Butte, Montana). Lesser amounts of copper are produced from hydrothermal veins, from copper associated with organic matter in redbeds, and from native copper. Successful recovery of copper as a by-product of manganese nodules from the sea floor may provide another source.

The world outlook for copper resources is favorable for at least fifty years. At the present rate of consumption, and as more countries become industrialized, many more deposits will be required. The potential of the USSR has barely been tapped, and the chances for additional porphyry coppers in the Western Hemisphere are good.

PLATE 12

The large open pit porphyry copper mine at Chino, New Mexico.
The pit is more than one mile across.

Nickel and Cobalt   Nickel and cobalt are discussed together because of their geochemical affinity and because they substitute for each other and for other elements such as iron (Fe^{2+}). In the absence of sulfur, both nickel and cobalt will substitute for Fe^{2+} and Mg^{2+} in olivines and pyroxenes in mafic and ultramafic rocks. When sulfur is present, their chalcophile nature causes both nickel and cobalt to be concentrated to a much greater degree in the sulfide minerals than in the silicates. If this were not the case, then nickel recovery would be very costly.

Consider the hypothetical case of equal amounts of nickel present in two bodies of a rock such as gabbro; the first contains no sulfur, and the second contains an appreciable amount of sulfur (see Figure 1–4). In the sulfur-free gabbro, both nickel and cobalt would substitute for iron and magnesium and would be strongly bonded to silica tetrahedra. Extraction of the nickel and cobalt would be uneconomic because the structure of the silicates is difficult to break down. In the second case the nickel and cobalt would be concentrated with the sulfur, and sulfide minerals could be separated from silicate with relative ease, allowing successful recovery of the metals.

If either gabbro or other nickel-bearing ultramafic to mafic rock were exposed to conditions favorable for formation of laterites, then nickel and cobalt would behave like iron and would be concentrated in the laterite. Thus, in addition to production from sulfide deposits in nick-

64

eliferous metallogenic regions, significant production comes from laterites as well.

The United States is almost solely dependent on imports of nickel from Canada, where the famous Sudbury deposit continues to account for much of the world's production. The Sudbury ores contain nickel-bearing pentlandite ($(Fe, Ni)_9S_8$) and chalcopyrite. The major rock type at Sudbury is norite (similar in composition to gabbro but with a different pyroxene as an essential mineral). Geologists believe that immiscible sulfide liquids separated from the silicate liquid as the rock crystallized and were concentrated by magmatic segregation. Copper is also produced at Sudbury, but the amounts do not rival those from the porphyry copper deposits.

Nickeliferous laterites are of two types. First, laterites rich in iron are commonly enriched in nickel if basic to ultramafic rocks were the ultimate source and the nickel is included in iron oxide-hydroxides. Second, a type of nickeliferous laterite contains a hydrated magnesium nickel silicate called garnierite. This mineral forms only over ultramafic rocks very rich in magnesium, enriched in nickel, and deficient in aluminum and iron. Not all the silica nor magnesium is removed before garnierite (stable under conditions for laterite formation) is formed. About 20 percent of the world's nickel production is from laterites of this type. Large resources are noted especially from New Caledonia and from the Philippines and Cuba. In the United States there is a relatively small deposit of nickeliferous garnierite at Riddle, Oregon. Because cobalt is always recovered along with nickel, these laterites will also yield cobalt.

PLATE 13

Nickel-rich laterite developing on top of ultramafic rocks in New Caledonia. (Courtesy of W. E. Elston.)

Nickel is used extensively in the steel industry for alloys. Roughly two-thirds of the total 350 million pounds (15,900 metric tons) of nickel consumed in the United States in 1974 was used in alloys. The remainder was used for electroplating and chemical uses. Cobalt, like nickel, is largely consumed in various alloys with much smaller but important uses in the paint industry, the chemical industry (including radioactive cobalt-60), and as feed additives. Cobalt is obtained as a by-product from nickel mining (Canada), copper mining (Zambia-Zaire), and iron mining (Finland). Because cobalt can oxidize to Co^{3+} and nickel cannot, it is possible that nongarnierite laterites will be greatly enriched in cobalt. If iron laterites are mined on a larger scale in the future, then cobalt production will increase proportionately.

Lead and Zinc   Lead and zinc are also discussed together because of their similar geochemical behavior. While lead and zinc are not as close in geochemical properties as nickel and cobalt, they are concentrated together for other reasons. Because Pb^{2+} is a much larger iron than Zn^{2+} (1.35 angstroms versus 0.80 angstrom, respectively), lead is concentrated in galena (PbS) and zinc in sphalerite (ZnS). This differs from nickel and cobalt, which usually occur in the same mineral. Both lead and zinc are lithophile as well as chalcophile. More importantly, they are commonly transported to about the same degree by chloride or carbonate complexes; this fact accounts in part for their close association. Production and consumption curves for lead and zinc are shown in Figures 4–9 and 4–10.

Uses for both lead and zinc are interesting. In addition to its well-known use in batteries and shielding materials, a principal use of lead was as a gasoline additive. This use is declining because of lead's toxicity. Increased use in industry and for shielding purposes, however, has offset this decline. Zinc, on the other hand, is used for alloys, brass, galvanizing iron, and in the chemical industry. It is the fourth among all metals in production (behind iron, aluminum, and copper). Its use as a galvanizing agent has made the classic "tin can" nearly obsolete, which is fortunate since tin is less abundant than zinc. Tin is resistant to corrosion, but it does not bind to iron and thus tends to spall off and allow corrosive attack of the underlying iron. Zinc meshes chemically into the iron so that spallation is prevented and the lifetime of the can is prolonged. This same use makes it desirable in corrosion-resistant alloys.

Five countries dominate both lead and zinc production. The leaders for lead are the United States, the USSR, Australia, Canada, and Peru. According to the U.S. Bureau of Mines, they produce more than 3.5 million metric tons. For zinc, the leading producers are Canada, the USSR, the United States, Australia, and Peru, which account for more than 5.6 million metric tons.

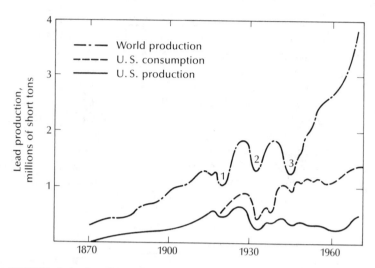

FIGURE 4–9 Lead production. The lows (1,2,3) in world production were due to World War I, the Great Depression, and World War II, respectively. It is also very clear that U.S. consumption is far greater than U.S. production—hence our reliance on imports. Recycling of lead has somewhat relieved our shortage of this metal.

Deposits of uniform, low-grade lead and zinc (analogous to porphyry coppers) are unknown, and expensive underground mining techniques must be used. Lead and zinc are mostly found in stratiform sedimentary deposits (but not usually at the surface) and as contact metamorphic or hydrothermal vein deposits.The hydrothermal veins are usually located near igneous rocks, with the exception of the extensive stratabound deposits in the tri-state (Missouri-Kansas-Oklahoma) district of the United States.

The most famous stratiform deposit is the Kupferschiefer deposit of north central Europe where both lead and zinc have been recovered along with copper. The zinc in this deposit is concentrated on the edges of the original sedimentary basin. Similar accumulations of zinc and lead have *not* been discovered in the Zambia-Zaire copper belt.

Contact metamorphic deposits are found in metasedimentary rocks close to igneous bodies where lead and zinc are separated from other metals by different transport mechanisms. Although often difficult to locate, these deposits are usually of a very high grade. Contact metamorphic deposits are irregular, especially when the ore is directly precipitated in fracture systems and replacement (or fracture filling) deposits result. They are also closely related to the intrusive igneous rocks. Common in the Western Hemisphere, deposits of this type are found in Mexico and in Utah and Nevada.

The lead and zinc deposits in the tri-state district (Missouri-Kansas-Oklahoma) are unique. These consist of irregular fracture-filling

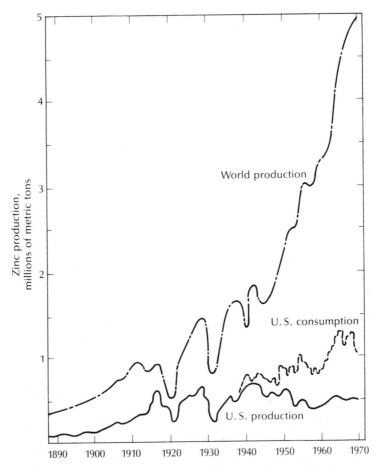

FIGURE 4–10 Zinc production. The production curves for zinc are very similar to those for lead because the two metals commonly occur in the same types of deposits. U.S. resources for zinc are favorable, yet our consumption exceeds production for economic reasons. Much of our zinc is contained in ore for which the extractive metallurgy is costly; and other deposits are located near urban centers, where environmental problems might arise. Thus it is actually cheaper to import much of our zinc and help the balance of trade.

veins rich in galena and sphalerite. No exposed parent igneous rocks are present. The host rock is typically carbonate which has been brecciated or in which the carbonate has been replaced by ore. Although the origin of these deposits is uncertain, recent work has established links between the ore and brines. The brines are possibly related to a complex widespread basin containing petroleum, evaporites, and other resources. It is also possible that some of the metals may have been introduced into such an environment from deep-seated metamorphic fluids resulting from even deeper magmatic processes. This is mentioned because of the great expanses of platform carbonate rocks which have not been explored for their metal content during petroleum or other nonmetal searches.

Finally, stratabound deposits of lead and zinc in metamorphic rocks are also common and economically important in many areas (e.g., Australia, New Brunswick, and British Columbia) as are stratiform deposits of the type found in Kuroko, Japan. The ore in the latter deposits is thought to be a product of complex submarine volcanism associated with plate tectonic processes.

Molybdenum   Molybdenum is normally present in molybdenite (MoS_2) because of its high charge (4+). Because of its small ionic radius (0.7 angstrom), Mo^{4+} is found associated with other chalcophile elements. Much of the world's molybdenum is found in a metallogenic belt which runs from Alaska, through Canada and the western United States, into Mexico (Figure 4–11). However, about 25 percent of all molybdenum is produced as a by-product from porphyry copper mining, even though it constitutes only about 0.02 percent of those rocks.

Molybdenum is used as an alloying agent with iron and steel. Extensive research is underway to find other uses for the metal because the United States has a surplus of reserves and resources. So far, molybdenum has been only moderately successful as a substitute for other metals. Because molybdenum is commonly disseminated throughout silicic igneous rocks, geologists are searching for "porphyry molybdenum" sources—not just for molybdenum, but also because the host rocks are theoretically capable of containing substantial amounts of scarce tin and tungsten. If discovered, the molybdenum mining might offset cost of tin and tungsten recovery.

Mercury   Mercury, although extremely rare, deserves special mention because U.S. supplies are virtually exhausted (the last operating mine closed in 1976), making the United States totally dependent upon imports. Nearly 70 percent of our imports come from Canada, Mexico, and Spain, with the other 30 percent from Algeria.* The Organization for Economic Cooperation and Development (OECD), headquartered in Algeria, was established in 1973 to control the price of mercury. If international conflict should occur (OPEC demands, for example), then OECD policy may have a pronounced effect on the supply of mercury to the United States. The distribution of mercury is shown in Figure 4–12.

---

*U.S. Bureau of Mines, *Minerals Yearbook*, 1976.

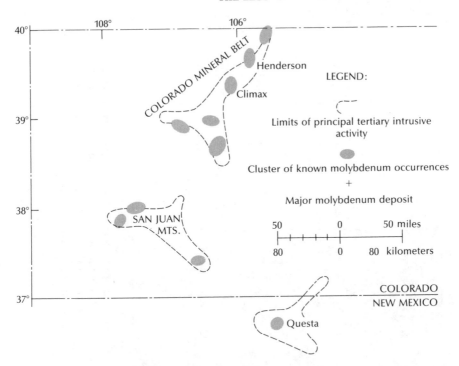

FIGURE 4–11 Major occurrences of molybdenum in the United States. This metallogenic province runs from Canada to Mexico and parallels the porphyry copper belt, which in turn parallels the subduction zone on the west coast of North America. Note the relatively close clustering of deposits. The United States is the world leader in molybdenum metal production, 25 percent of which is a byproduct of copper mining.

Substitutes for mercury, a liquid at room temperature, are difficult or impossible to make. If more mercury cannot be found, its uses as an electrolytic catalyst for chlorine and caustic soda production, in electrical apparatus, for paint ingredients, and in industrial and chemical applications could be in jeopardy. For some of these uses (especially in the chemical industry) there are no known substitutes for mercury.

In the United States, as elsewhere, the chief ore mineral for mercury is cinnabar (HgS). Deposits of cinnabar are located chiefly in the Coast ranges of California and nearby in Nevada, Oregon, and Washington. Not only has mining ceased but resources from this area are subeconomic at best. Many of the Mississippi Valley lead-zinc deposits contain appreciable amounts of mercury and, if worked on a large scale after metallurgical difficulties are overcome, may provide a long-range resource for domestic mercury. In the meantime the United States has entered into joint ventures with Canada and Mexico.

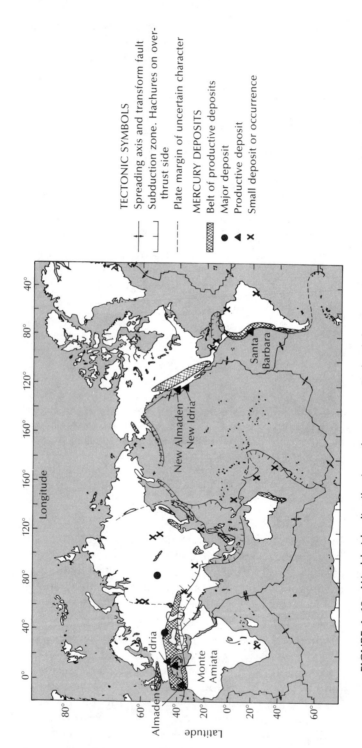

FIGURE 4–12 Worldwide distribution of mercury. Each of the cross-hatched areas represents an area where mercury can be mined economically. Such areas, commonly restricted to particular rock types and tectonic features, are known as metallogenic provinces. Most of the mercury metallogenic provinces follow zones of subduction. The rich deposits of the U.S. west coast have been mined out, so we rely totally on imports for mercury.

TECTONIC SYMBOLS

Spreading axis and transform fault
Subduction zone. Hachures on over-thrust side
Plate margin of uncertain character

MERCURY DEPOSITS

Belt of productive deposits
Major deposit
Productive deposit
Small deposit or occurrence

Scarce Metals Associated with Oxygen

Many metals tend to be associated with oxygen, either in oxides or in silicates, rather than with sulfur. Consequently, many of these elements will not be concentrated but will be widely disseminated throughout typical rocks.

Chromium   Chromium is concentrated as chromite ($FeCr_2O_4$) by magmatic segregation and is abundant worldwide. Domestic resources are small,* however, and the United States relies on imports from the USSR, several countries in Africa, and the Philippines. Deposits in the Western Hemisphere are small and subeconomic except for some in Cuba.

Chromium is used for ferroalloys, for furnace linings, and in the chemical industry. There are no adequate substitutes for chromium, which can withstand high temperatures and resist corrosion. Since chromium is found principally in ultramafic rocks, chromite deposits are sought in these types of rocks. Again, successful mining of sea floor manganese nodules may provide another source of chromium.

Tin and Tungsten   The United States imports large amounts of tin and tungsten, although the situation is somewhat better for tungsten than for tin. The mineral cassiterite (SnO_2), from which tin is obtained, is widely disseminated in acid igneous rocks. Because cassiterite is resistant to weathering, it is concentrated in placers. Tin is used in tinplate, solder, alloys, bronze, and in the chemical industry and is an excellent coating for other metals because of its resistance to weathering.

Tin is found principally in two metallogenic belts. In eastern Asia tin is found in a belt from the Malaysian Peninsula into Indonesia, and another belt runs from Bolivia into Peru. Prior to 1975 a U.S. company had developed what might have been the world's largest tin operation in southeastern Asia, but a coup in Thailand rendered the U.S. operation useless.

Tungsten is found in nature as wolframite ($FeWO_4$) and scheelite ($CaWO_4$), neither of which is abundant in the United States. The major metallogenic belt for tungsten occurs in eastern Asia in a belt running from Korea through China to Malaya. Therefore, the United States must import most of its tungsten. Conventional uses include cutting devices of tungsten carbide (45 percent), alloys (50 percent), and other uses (5 percent), according to the U.S. Geological Survey.[†]

---

*Large, low-grade deposits such as those of the Stillwater Complex, Montana, await better technology for chromium extraction.

[†]U.S. Geological Survey, op. cit.

METALS

There is now an increasing demand for tungsten in the aerospace industry because tungsten alloys are more suited than other metals for extreme conditions.

Figure 4–8 shows that tin and tungsten are spatially related to subduction zones and in silicic-plutonic rocks. This has led to increased exploration in similar settings on a worldwide scale.

Beryllium, Niobium, and Tantalum   Other scarce metals such as beryllium, niobium, and tantalum are concentrated in special rocks commonly formed as residue of magmatic crystallization. These elements do not fit easily into the structures of the common rock-forming minerals and do not possess chalcophile tendencies. Consequently, niobium and tantalum are concentrated in carbonatites associated with alkaline-igneous rocks and in pegmatites associated with silicic-igneous rocks. Beryllium is commonly concentrated in pegmatites but may also be concentrated in some volcanic-silicic rocks.

Beryllium metal is used in the aerospace industry and in increasing amounts by the nuclear industry because it does not readily absorb neutrons. Beryllium alloys with steel, aluminum, or magnesium are now being used, and beryllium oxide is valuable to the electrical industry and is used in nuclear reactor fuel elements. Additional uses for beryl and beryllium compounds are found in the chemical industry. Only in the last seven years has U.S. production based on discovery and exploitation of new beryllium resources caused imports to drop to below 50 percent.

Niobium is concentrated in carbonatites to a much greater degree than is tantalum, which is concentrated more often in pegmatites. Both are found in placer deposits throughout the world. Niobium sources outside the United States dwarf domestic resources, but the U.S. Geological Survey estimates that there is enough niobium to meet our needs to the year 2000. Tantalum supplies may dwindle before that time. Niobium at present is used for superalloys in the construction and aerospace industries. In the future, it may be used in materials to control nuclear fusion energy; if so, then U.S. niobium supplies are woefully inadequate.

Most of the tantalum is consumed by the electronics industry, and the remainder is used for superalloys in the aerospace industry and lesser amounts used as tantalum carbide in cutting tools. The chemical industry uses a small amount. Increased reliance on imports is projected for both metals.

Vanadium   Vanadium is one of the few elements of which the United States has an adequate supply. Although used primarily for alloys and in the chemical industry, vanadium is presently being used in the iron and steel industry in amounts double that used in the chemical industry. But more uses are being found in the chemical industry, so this balance is likely to shift to more nonferrous uses.

Vanadium minerals are commonly found in carbonatites. In fact, the vanadium content of the Magnet Cove, Arkansas, carbonatite may be the single largest potential resource of vanadium in the United States. But, unlike other elements with many oxidation states (e.g., niobium and tantalum) which remain locked in complex oxy-salts, vanadium minerals weather rather easily and are transported in solution along with uranium and smaller amounts of elements such as selenium, arsenic, and molybdenum. When reducing conditions are encountered after sedimentation, vanadium is reduced and precipitated as vanadium minerals or in vanadium-rich minerals, commonly in association with uranium and molybdenum in sandstone deposits. Deposits of this type are common on the Colorado Plateau, where we obtain most of our vanadium (including vanadium as a by-product of uranium milling).

The Scarce Precious Metals

Although gold, silver, and platinum all occur as native metal, most gold and silver is produced as a by-product of copper mining or lead-zinc mining operations. Porphyry coppers account for virtually all domestic gold production; these, plus lead-zinc operations, account for well over 75 percent of domestic silver production. Gold, like the platinoids (platinum, rhodium, osmium, and iridium), is commonly enriched in placer deposits in the United States, but they are too small and too sporadically distributed to be significant in terms of national needs.

Gold   As the metal chosen as the monetary base for international trade, gold supplies are justifiably meager. In terms of its use as a metal, gold does have many substitutes. An abundant gold supply certainly does not guarantee world power to any country, typified by South Africa, which has over 50 percent of the positive or probable gold reserves in the world. Gold in the United States, in addition to that from porphyry coppers (and the spotty placers), occurs in hydrothermally deposited gold disseminated in sedimentary rocks in Nevada and possibly elsewhere. As prices continue to climb it is likely that gold production will increase, but probably not enough to offset our 3:1 ratio of imports to domestic production for nonmonetary purposes. Data for the production, reserves, and ores of gold are shown in Figure 4–13.

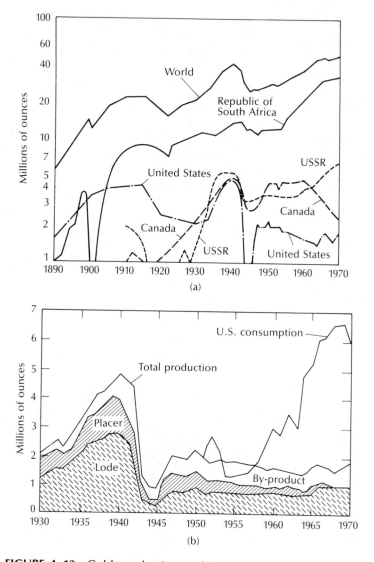

FIGURE 4–13 Gold production and distribution. Part (a) shows gold reserves and production; part (b) shows the amount produced for each type of gold ore. Most gold is actually produced from by-products of porphyry copper mining and from small, rich lode deposits. Placer deposits are, despite their historical glamour, of very little importance.

Silver Silver more commonly occurs in sulfides than as the native metal, but it is usually considered with gold and the platinoids when describing production. Silver is used largely in the photographic and electrical industries where supply cannot meet demand. Despite production from copper- and lead-zinc operations, the United States must still import most of its silver. Although silver is widespread, it is so rare that unless prices increase the United States will continue to import to meet national needs.

Platinum   The platinoids are usually found in ultramafic rocks or in placer deposits derived from these rocks. The largest reserves of platinum and associated metals is in southern Africa, but the Soviet Union also contains moderately large supplies in the Urals. Smaller nondomestic sources include Canada and Colombia. In the United States, platinum and associated metals are recovered from serpentine belts in California, Oregon, Washington, and Alaska, and Montana contains low-grade reserves from layered gabbro and peridotite. The United States produces only two percent of the amount of platinoids consumed each year in the aerospace, chemical, and petroleum industries and for metallurgical applications. A small amount is used for jewelry and other minor applications in various fields.

Despite its scarcity in nature, the platinoids are critical to specific, highly technical applications for aerospace and electrical research and development, and no adequate substitutes have been found. Because overseas imports may be stopped in the foreseeable future, we are trying to find ways to process low-grade platinum-bearing rocks.

Milling

Milling refers to the processes by which the metal (or compound) is concentrated and removed from the ore.* For sulfide ore treatment, the rock is first crushed to a fine size and then mixed with any of a number of organic compounds (such as xanthates) in vats of water. The sulfides are fixed on the surface of the organic matter and rise to the surface of the water, while the silicate and oxide fractions sink to the bottom. This process is known as *flotation*. The sulfide-rich froth is then skimmed off, and the metal is extracted by electrolytic methods (see Additional Readings). The importance of sulfides in concentrating trace chalcophile elements is illustrated in Figure 4–14.

Once the metals have been separated from the sulfur in retorts, various metals can be separated from each other because they possess slightly different electrical properties. Very fine separations can be made. By-products from this purification amount to significant production of such metals as molybdenum, gold, and silver.

For some iron ores, finely crushed rock is mixed with clay and rolled into small spheres. The iron-rich spheres are separated from

---

*A thorough treatment of various milling techniques is beyond the scope of this book. However, some useful references are listed in Additional Readings.

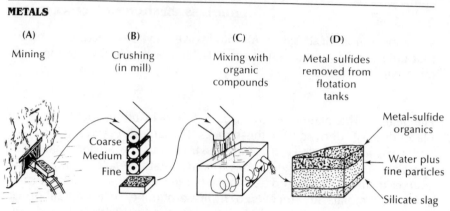

(A)   (B)   (C)   (D)

Mining   Crushing   Mixing with   Metal sulfides
           (in mill)   organic   removed from
                            compounds   flotation
                                             tanks

FIGURE 4–14 Metal sulfide recovery. Ore from the mine (A) is first crushed (B) and then mixed with a water solvent rich in organic compounds (C). The organic compounds affix themselves to the metal sulfides and, because of their low density, float to the surface (D) where the froth of metal sulfide and organic matter can be skimmed off. The metal is then removed from the sulfide by a combination of roasting and electrolysis.

the iron-poor material by magnetic separation and then fed to blast furnaces. For uranium (see Chapter 7), the finely crushed rock is treated with oxidizing agents that dissolve the uranium ore and some other elements. The solution containing the oxidized uranium is then passed through ion-exchange media in successive steps. Vanadium is separated by another chemical treatment until "yellowcake," the popular name for bright yellow uranium compounds containing 90 to 97 percent uranium, is produced. The efficiency of milling is remarkable when we remember that the initial ore may have contained only about 0.03 percent uranium.

Selected data for the less abundant and scarce metals are summarized in Table 4–2, and Table 4–3 outlines U.S. and world production of the more common metals. Figure 4–15 then compares U.S. consumption and production with world production.

TABLE 4–2 Less abundant and scarce metals.

Elements	Mineral	Formula	Occurrence or Remarks
Manganese	Pyrolusite	MnO_2	Sedimentary or residual deposits
	Manganese nodules	Variable	Sea floor
	Rhodochrosite	$MnCO_3$	Residual deposits
Chromium	Chromite	$FeCr_2O_4$	Igneous rocks
	Manganese nodules	Variable	By-product of Mn mining
Copper	Chalcopyrite	$CuFeS_2$	Porphyry coppers; other sulfides deposits

TABLE 4–2   (continued)

Elements	Mineral	Formula	Occurrence or Remarks
	Chalcocite	Cu_2S	Porphyry coppers; other sulfides deposits
	Copper-pyrite	$(Fe, Cu) S_2$	Porphyry coppers; other sulfides deposits
	Enargite	Cu_3AsS_4	Porphyry coppers; other sulfides deposits
	Bornite	Cu_5FeS_4	Porphyry coppers; other sulfides deposits
Nickel and Cobalt	Pentlandite	$(Fe, Ni, Co)_9S_8$	Sulfide deposits in gabbros
	Garnierite	Ni (Co)-silicate	Laterites developed over ultramafic rocks
Lead	Galena	PbS	Sulfide deposits; by-product from porphyry coppers
Zinc	Sphalerite	ZnS	Sulfide deposits and by-products of porphyry coppers
Molyb-denum	Molybdenite	MoS_2	Sulfide deposits with granitic rocks; also with porphyry coppers
Mercury	Cinnabar	HgS	With alpine serpentines in volcanic terraines
Tin	Cassiterite	SnO_2	Granitic rocks; placers
Tungsten	Scheelite	$CaWO_4$	Related to silicic, plutonic rocks
	Wolframite	$FeWO_4$	Related to silicic plutonic rocks
Beryllium	Beryl	$Be_3Al_2Si_6O_{18}$	Pegmatites; some volcanics
Niobium	Niobium oxides; niobates	Complex	Pegmatites; carbonatites
Tantalum	Tantalum oxides; tantalates	Complex	Pegmatites; carbonatites
Vanadium	Vanadium oxides; silicates	Complex	Sandstone V, U deposits; carbonatites
Gold	Sulfides or native gold	—	By-product of porphyry coppers; volcanics; *very little* from placers
Silver	Sulfides; some native silver	Complex	Sulfide deposits; porphyry copper by-product
Platinum (and related metals)	Native platinum	Pt	Ultramafic rocks; placers

SOURCE: U.S. Geological Survey, op. cit.

TABLE 4–3 U.S. and world production of metals (thousands of short tons unless otherwise specified).

Minerals	1975			1976		
	World Prod.	U.S. Prod.	U.S. Percent of World Prod.	World Prod.	U.S. Prod.	U.S. Percent of World Prod.
Metals, Smelter Basis						
Aluminum	13,352	3,879	29	13,774	4,251	31
Copper	7,793	1,447	19	8,164	1,535	19
Iron, pig	528,861	79,721	15	549,298	86,848	16
Lead	3,656	636	17	3,788	653	17
Magnesium	138	NA	NA	148	NA	NA
Steel ingots and castings	712,556	116,642	16	748,492	128,000	17
Tin (metric tons)	230,596	6,500	3	228,856	5,700	2
Zinc	5,592	438	8	5,978	499	8
Metals, Mine Basis						
Arsenic, white (tons)	46,449	NA	NA	39,919	NA	NA
Chromite	9,071	?	?	9,492	?	?
Cobalt (contained) (short tons)	32,462	?	?	28,681	?	?
Copper (content of ore and concentrate)	7,672	1,413	18	8,213	1,606	20
Gold (thousand troy ounces)	38,676	1,052	3	39,883	1,048	3
Iron ore (thousand long tons)	887,389	78,866	9	881,028	79,993	9
Lead (content of ore and concentrate	3,750	621	17	3,701	610	16
Manganese ore (35% or more Mn)	27,076	?	?	27,292	?	?
Mercury (thousand 76-lb flasks)	252	7	3	244	23	9
Molybdenum (content of ore and concentrate) (thousand pounds)	176,713	105,980	60	191,287	113,233	59
Nickel (content of ore and concentrate)	868	17	2	886	16	2
Platinum-group metals (thousand troy ounces)	5,714	19	?	5,992	6	?
Silver (thousand troy ounces)	297,882	34,938	12	304,899	34,328	11
Tin (content of ore and concentrate) (metric tons)	224,180	NA	NA	225,755	NA	NA

TABLE 4–3 (continued)

Minerals	1975			1976		
	World Prod.	U.S. Prod.	U.S. Percent of World Prod.	World Prod.	U.S. Prod.	U.S. Percent of World Prod.
Titanium concentrates: Ilmenite	3,218	717	22	3,512	652	19
Rutile	417	NA	NA	471	NA	NA
Tungsten concentrate (contained tungsten) (thousand pounds)	84,262	5,588	7	91,845	5,830	6
Uranium oxide (U_3O_8) (short tons)	26,677	11,600	43	30,100	12,700	42
Vanadium (content of ore and concentrate) (short tons)	23,201	4,743	20	25,950	7,376	28
Zinc (content of ore and concentrate)	6,391	469	7	6,462	485	8

NA = Not available
? = Data not available
SOURCE: Data from U.S. Bureau of Mines, *Minerals Yearbook*, 1976.

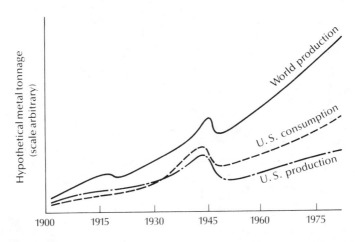

FIGURE 4–15 Production and consumption of a hypothetical metal. These curves are typical of the production-consumption curves for many metals. World production typically dropped off during and just after both world wars (and possibly around 1930 due to the Great Depression). U.S. consumption surpassed U.S. production just before and just after World War II. Increased technology created more uses for most metals, hence a continued increase in consumption. Lack of reserves and inflated mining costs in the United States cause us to rely on imports to meet our demands.

Nonmetals for Agriculture and the Chemical Industry

Nonmetals include those elements and compounds that are used for reasons other than their metallic properties. Most nonmetals are used in agriculture and the chemical industry.

First we will discuss the formation and distribution of certain types of sedimentary deposits. These deposits include marine and nonmarine evaporites, salt domes, and phosphorous-rich sedimentary rocks.

Sea water contains about 3.5 percent dissolved solids by weight. These are dominated by sodium and chlorine (as part of dissolved NaCl) as follows:

Cations		Anions	
Na:	30.6%	Cl:	55.1%
Mg:	3.7%	S:	2.7%
Ca:	1.2%	Br:	0.2%
K:	1.1%		

All other species—including dissolved carbon dioxide (CO_2) as the ions HCO_3^- (bicarbonate), H_2CO_3 (carbonic acid), and CO_3^{2-} (carbonate)—are of minor importance. The elements occurring as cations are present as simple M^+ or M^{2+} species, while chlorine as Cl^- dominates the anions. Sulfur, however, occurs as the SO_4^{2-} (sulfate) ion.

These elements are more concentrated in the earth's crust than others because weathering of most crustal rocks produces clay containing most of the released silica and alumina. Some dissolved silica is present as H_4SiO_4, but virtually all alumina is insoluble; that aluminum not removed when clay minerals are formed is released as amorphous $Al(OH)_3$. Similarly, iron oxidizes from soluble Fe^{2+} to insoluble Fe^{3+} as $Fe(OH)_3$

and thus is not concentrated in sea water. Potassium (K^+) is preferentially incorporated into clay minerals relative to sodium (Na^+), which explains why sodium is enriched in sea water while potassium-rich clay minerals form in river or deltaic environments. Similarly, calcium (Ca^{2+}) is more easily fixed in clay minerals than is magnesium (Mg^{2+}); hence magnesium is more abundant than calcium in sea water. Because most chlorine, sulfur, and bromine are added to the oceans by submarine volcanism, these elements as soluble species are abundant in sea water and rare in crustal rocks.

Evaporites

Mineral solubilities differ radically. For example, $CaCO_3$ is less soluble than $CaSO_4$, and both are less soluble than NaCl. As sea water evaporates (Figure 5–1), dissolved salts are concentrated until they precipitate. However, evaporite formation involves processes more complex than mere evaporation of sea water. In the classic model of *marine evaporite* formation (Figure 5–2) a reef or shoal restricts sea water. Normally this occurs under very warm conditions (within 35 degrees latitude north or south of the equator) or less commonly under cold conditions but with very high winds (Figure 5–3). Seas overrun the barrier periodically and dissolve some of the more soluble salts. Eventually accumulations of evaporite minerals result (Figure 5–4). Due to their very great solubility, potassium- and magnesium-bearing salts and halite (NaCl) are rare in marine evaporites. The usual marine evaporite sequence consists of carbonate rocks and anhydrite or gypsum. (Whether anhydrite or gypsum is present depends on temperature, pressure due to burial, and availability of groundwaters.) In areas where evaporation has been relatively uninterrupted, halite will form interlayered with anhydrite or gypsum. Finally, in almost totally uninterrupted sequences, potassium (usually sylvite, KCl) and magnesium salts will be found interlayered with halite. This model for evaporite formation assumes shallow deposition.

The geologic record, however, indicates that some marine evaporites are formed at relatively great depths in the oceans. A dense brine (see Figure 5–2) underlying less dense, near-normal sea water may form. As the near-normal sea water evaporates, early-formed crystals sink into the brine where they may dissolve and make the brine even denser. Other salts also crystallize at the bottom of the brine layer. This model indicates that evaporites can be deposited not only at depth but over wide areas, which would explain why very large deposits of evaporites occur in various areas in the world.

It is interesting to note that the dense brine is often rich in organic matter from the aquatic organism residue and also somewhat rich

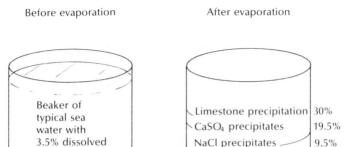

Before evaporation · After evaporation

Beaker of typical sea water with 3.5% dissolved salts

Limestone precipitation 30%
CaSO₄ precipitates 19.5%
NaCl precipitates 9.5%
K, Mg salts precipitate 2 – 4%

FIGURE 5–1 Usiglio's evaporation experiments. The Italian scientist J. Usiglio conducted a series of studies on seawater evaporation in the late 1840s. He found that normal evaporation led to some calcium carbonate (i.e., limestone) formation after about 70 percent of the seawater had been evaporated. Gypsum formed after 80 percent had evaporated, and common table salt, halite (NaCl), formed after 90.5 percent evaporation. Not until 96 to 98 percent had evaporated did potassium and magnesium salts appear. In nature rocks formed by evaporation follow a typical sequence of thick layers of limestone and gypsum (or anhydrite) followed by minor amounts of halite and rarely sylvite (KCl).

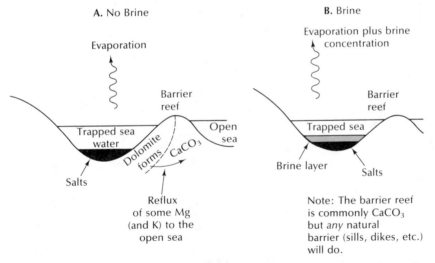

A. No Brine

Evaporation

Barrier reef

Trapped sea water

Open sea

Dolomite forms / CaCO₃

Salts

Reflux of some Mg (and K) to the open sea

B. Brine

Evaporation plus brine concentration

Barrier reef

Trapped sea

Brine layer

Salts

Note: The barrier reef is commonly CaCO₃ but *any* natural barrier (sills, dikes, etc.) will do.

FIGURE 5–2 Marine evaporite formation. Under natural conditions evaporites may form from either condition **A** (simple evaporation) or **B** (evaporation plus formation of a brine layer). Thick layers of limestone (at 70 percent evaporation) can accumulate before gypsum (at 80 percent evaporation) starts to form. Flooding at about the time gypsum is starting to form will precipitate more limestone. Hence alternating layers of limestone and gypsum are the rule. Similarly, at about 90 percent evaporation, alternating layers of halite and gypsum are noted; and, near total evaporation, sylvite and magnesium salts are interlayered with halite. Some of the magnesium is not incorporated into the evaporite and causes dolomitization of the barrier reef, as shown in condition **A**.

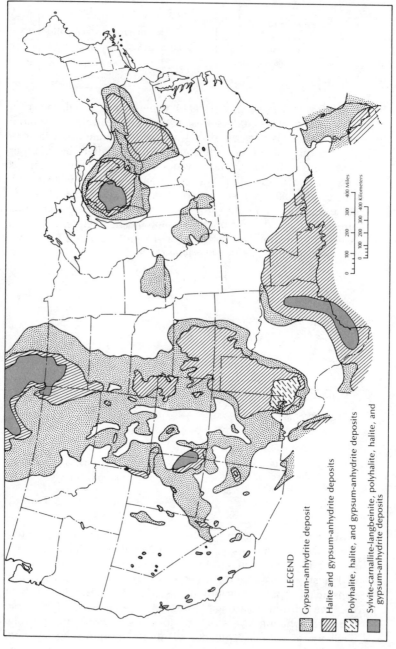

LEGEND

Gypsum-anhydrite deposit

Halite and gypsum-anhydrite deposits

Polyhalite, halite, and gypsum-anhydrite deposits

Sylvite-carnallite-langbeinite, polyhalite, halite, and gypsum-anhydrite deposits

FIGURE 5–3 Marine evaporite occurrences in the United States. This map shows the abundance of marine evaporites and concentrations of potash-rich (sylvite) areas. The potash deposits of New Mexico are the largest producers in the United States. However, the potash deposits of the Williston Basin (which extend northward from the Montana-North Dakota border into Saskatchewan) are just now reaching full capacity. Since evaporites are also considered for storage of radioactive waste, this map shows where

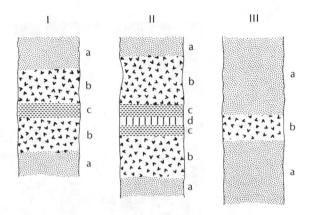

FIGURE 5–4 Common marine evaporite column. Column I shows the most common evaporite sequence mined for commercial purposes: alternating layers of limestone (a), anhydrite (b), and halite (c). Column II shows the most rare sequence: alternating layers of limestone (a), anhydrite (b), halite (c), and sylvite (d). Here evaporation has occurred very slowly without much influx of new water so that potassium and magnesium salts will form. Column III shows a typical evaporite sequence at the edge of a basin margin where only limestone (a) and minor anhydrite (b) are found. Recognition of the columns (columns I and III) away from the center of the basin (column II) may allow successful prospecting for potassium and magnesium salts (column II).

in reduced sulfur species (usually aqueous H_2S). The organic matter may under special conditions accumulate as oil and gas, while small amounts of H_2S may react with metal ions such as Cu^{2+}, Pb^{2+}, and Zn^{2+}, allowing layered sulfide deposits to form. Thus both petroleum and metal sulfides are occasionally associated with marine evaporites.

Nonmarine evaporites result when water evaporates from locally restricted seas. Because of their smaller size and limited exchange with normal sea water, the chemical composition of nonmarine evaporites is extremely variable. The dominant anion is sulfate, followed by lesser amounts of borate or carbonate ions. The amount of chlorine present as Cl^- is very small; that is, the chlorine comes from continental rocks and not from submarine volcanism. The total amount of carbonate is small as well. Hence nonmarine evaporites typically include sodium carbonates, sodium sulfates, sodium borates, complex sodium, calcium salts, and in general salts which reflect the local highland areas that have been weathered away. Thus, a limestone-rich source area would provide abundant Ca^{2+} and HCO_3^- for subsequent nonmarine carbonates (and gypsum if enough sulfate is present) to form. In contrast, weathering of granitic highlands would produce deposits rich in sodium sulfates and carbonates. The same general rules still apply concerning the insoluble

NONMETALS FOR AGRICULTURE AND THE CHEMICAL INDUSTRY

PLATE 14

Magnesium-potassium-sulfate stalactites forming from brine seeps in an underground potash mine near Carlsbad, New Mexico. The source of the brine is the evaporite, not surface waters.

nature of silica, alumina, K^+, and Fe^{3+} due to clay mineral formation and hydroxide precipitation. Only the concentration of magnesium is difficult to predict. Some magnesium may be fixed in clay minerals, but some will also reach the restricted basin and later be incorporated into various salts. In short, the sequence of nonmarine evaporite minerals is—while largely unpredictable on a general scale—very different from marine evaporites. Conditions for nonmarine evaporite formation are illustrated in Figure 5–5.

Potassium

Potassium, largely as sylvite (KCl), is a vital fertilizer component. Although potassium is one of the eight most abundant elements in the earth's crust, it is locked up in common rock-forming silicate minerals or fixed in clay minerals during weathering so that essentially none is available as a soil nutrient. Sylvite in marine evaporites is often pure, relatively easy to mine, and can be easily treated to separate the potassium from the chlorine. In many evaporites containing sylvite, other complex potassium and magnesium salts (usually as sulfates) are also found. Langbeinite,

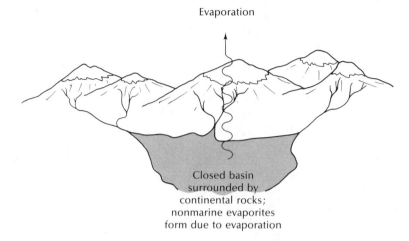

Evaporation

Closed basin
surrounded by
continental rocks;
nonmarine evaporites
form due to evaporation

FIGURE 5–5 Formation of nonmarine evaporites. Nonmarine evaporites may form anywhere a restricted (closed) drainage basin is found surrounded by continental rocks. Nonmarine evaporites, unlike marine evaporites, possess very complex chemistries due to the varied composition of rocks being weathered around the closed basin.

polyhalite, and kainite are usually associated with sylvite and may be used as ore. For example, because langbeinite has less potassium than sylvite, it is mined as the prime potassium ore only when the market price of potassium increases.

PLATE 15

Underground view of pure sylvite (KCl, or potash ore) from a depth of 2100 feet (640 meters) near Carlsbad, New Mexico. The chisel is 8 inches (20 centimeters) long. This bed, and others like it, extend laterally for thousands of square kilometers.

NONMETALS FOR AGRICULTURE AND THE CHEMICAL INDUSTRY

During World War I, Germany's Kaiser Wilhelm shut off the German potassium supply to the rest of the world. At that time, the famous salt deposits at Stassfurt provided much of the world's potash. If World War I had lasted much longer, this plan might actually have caused the intended starvation. But because of Germany's action, the rest of the world realized that vigorous exploration for new potash deposits was needed. Many countries, including the United States, discovered abundant potash deposits in the 1920s and had them operating by the 1930s—just in time for the Great Depression. Presently, the U.S. potash industry must compete with cheaper imports from even larger deposits in Saskatchewan. This is shown schematically in Figure 5–6, where production curves and export-import data are shown for potash, nitrogen, and phosphorus.

Although MACD figures (see Chapter 1) for potassium are not given by the U.S. Geological Survey, it is safe to assign the values of II for both identified and hypothetical resources. These figures are likely to improve in the twenty-first century. The availability of Canadian potash will probably meet many U.S. requirements, thus slowing exploration and development activities in the United States somewhat. On a worldwide

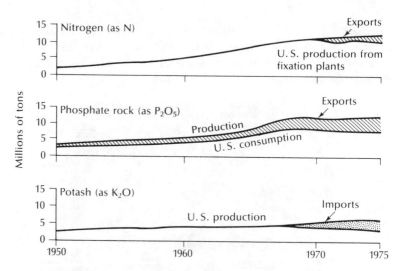

FIGURE 5–6 Nitrogen, phosphorus, and potassium production. "NPK" refers to the elements nitrogen (N), phosphorus (P), and potassium (K). Nitrogen is removed from the atmosphere by conversion plants, hence our supplies are enormous. Phosphate rock refers to marine phosphorites (apatite-rich) from which phosphorus can be extracted. The United States contains abundant reserves and resources of phosphate rocks, principally in Florida and in some nonmarine evaporites in the western United States. Of the NPK triad, only potash is imported, because cheaper potash is available from the extensive deposits in Saskatchewan.

basis, however, shortages are likely in areas where evaporites are scarce. Exports to these areas will no doubt come from Australia, northern Africa, and parts of Asia.

PLATE 16

Head frame and hoist at the Duval potash mine near Carlsbad, New Mexico. The ore occurs at a depth of over 2000 feet (610 meters). This area is the leading producer of potash ore in the United States.

Nitrogen

Most nitrogen was recovered from nitrate deposits or indirectly from commercial fertilizers until recovery from the atmosphere became practical. Nitrates are extremely soluble and are found only in very arid parts of the world. The largest deposits occur in the Atacama desert of Chile, where total precipitation from 1900 to 1970 was only 5 inches (13 centimeters). Chilean deposits still account for some 900,000 tons per year (817,000 metric tons)—about one-eleventh the amount of nitrogen produced in the United States. Figure 5–6 shows that we export a considerable amount.

Nitrogen used in the United States is now recovered by the Haber-Bosch process, which is also used to remove nitrogen from coal during coking. This process is summarized in the following equation:

$$N_2 + 3H_2 = 2NH_3 \text{ (ammonia gas)}$$

Ammonia produced in this way is usually added to croplands as ammonium sulfate or some other salt of ammonia, sometimes as ammonium nitrate or ammonium phosphate (which also adds phosphorus).

There is a move underway to recycle waste from feedlots and similar sources for nitrogen, thus preventing waste from affecting natural waters. When waste is not treated, plants use the nitrogen and eventually choke streams and ponds. Thus failure to recycle waste is doubly damning: Not only are we failing to take advantage of a ready supply of nitrogen, but we are also contaminating very valuable waters.

Phosphorus

Although phosphorus is abundant, it is unevenly distributed throughout the world. Typically, it is concentrated in sedimentary formations close to evaporites or other marine sedimentary formations. In the United States, the Phosphoria formation covers 100,000 square miles (259,000 square kilometers) and is 450 feet (135 meters) thick, with a phosphate bed 3 feet (1 meter) thick. This deposit was formed in a large sea which once covered parts of Montana, Idaho, Colorado, Utah, Wyoming, and Nevada. The Phosphoria formation, however, is still largely undeveloped. Most U.S. production comes from the older, more extensively developed marine phosphorite deposits in Tennessee and Florida. The main mineral which provides phosphorus in these formations is apatite, $Ca_5(PO_4)_3(OH)$, which also includes some fluorine (i.e., F^- for OH^-).

Prior to the discovery and widespread use of marine evaporites, the principal sources of phosphorus were guano and secondary apatite recovery from igneous rocks. At present, 75 percent of the world's phosphorus comes from marine phosphate rocks, about 16 percent from igneous apatite (usually as a by-product of other mining ventures), and the remaining 9 percent from guano deposits, mostly in small newly discovered deposits in the southern Pacific Ocean region. While the United States leads in world production (see Figure 5–6), it is closely followed by the Soviet Union. Other significant production comes from Morocco and Tunisia. Although identified phosphorus resources in the United States are given MACD figures of II and I, the existence of the Phosphoria formation accounts for a MACD figure of I for undiscovered resources (see Table 1–1). Major phosphorus shortages in the twenty-first century have been predicted, but this may be overcome by new ways of economically recovering phosphorus from sea water and nonmarine sediments. Recovery of phosphorus has been another test of technological expertise. Normal insoluble apatite leached with sulfuric acid forms soluble $Ca(H_2PO_4)_2$, known as *superphosphate*. This material can be added directly to soil or, when treated with ammonia, can replace the calcium to form ammonium superphosphate—an excellent soil nutrient.

Sulfur

About 60 percent of all sulfur produced is used directly in agriculture as soil additives (40%) and indirectly as insecticides or fungicides (20%). Because it occurs in many different places, sulfur has MACD figures of I for identified resources and I for hypothetical resources. These figures are not likely to change in the twenty-first century.

Worldwide, roughly 80 percent of all sulfur comes from three sources in about equal amounts: (1) from salt domes; (2) from the petroleum industry; and (3) as a by-product of metal sulfide mining. Other minor sources include sulfur from volcanic rocks and native sulfur. Sulfur from salt domes is the least expensive in terms of mining costs, while native sulfur is the most expensive source.

Recovery from Salt Domes

Of the 200 salt domes found in the Gulf of Mexico during petroleum exploration, roughly 10 percent contain commercial accumulations of sulfur. Salt domes are formed by salts forced upward through rapidly accumulating sediments due to the low density of evaporite minerals. This process is especially active in the Gulf of Mexico where tremendous amounts of sediment are being deposited, thus exerting a large lithostatic load on buried salt deposits. Part of these salt deposits is forced upward as a plastic mass through the sediments. Rocks are typically fractured during the process, and sulfur slows into the fractured rock.

Sulfur from salt domes is recovered by the Frasch process (Figure 5–7). In this process a pipe consisting of three concentric cylinders is drilled into the salt dome. Hot water forced down the outermost cylinder melts the native sulfur, which flows toward the middle cylinder by a combination of gravity flow and pumping. The innermost cylinder is used to inject a mixture of superheated air and steam into the molten sulfur to help it flow upward and remain in the molten state until it reaches the surface. Here the molten sulfur can either be allowed to solidify or it can be poured directly into specially designed railroad cars and transported as a liquid to its final destination. One major advantage of sulfur from salt domes is its purity. Whereas many forms of native sulfur contain numerous trace elements, the sulfur from salt domes is essentially free of contaminants.

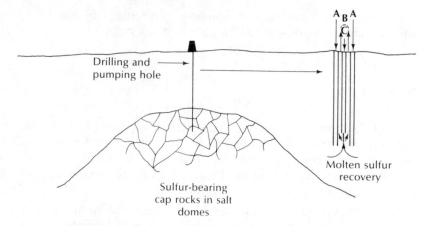

FIGURE 5–7 The Frasch process. A concentric pipe is inserted into sulfur-rich cap rocks found in many salt domes off the coasts of Louisiana, Texas, and Mississippi. Hot water, injected through the outer part of the pipe (A), melts the sulfur in the fractured rock. Because of its lower density, the molten sulfur moves to the recovery part of the pipe (B), where it is mixed with superheated air from the innermost part of the pipe (C) to keep the sulfur molten until it is recovered at the surface.

Recovery from Petroleum

Sulfur is recovered from petroleum processes in two ways, each equally important. In the first method, copious quantities of hydrogen sulfide (H_2S) are removed from a poisonous sour-crude gas. The gas is then oxidized to yield native sulfur. In the second method, abundant organic sulfur that has been combined with organic carbonaceous matter must be removed before the petroleum products are clean enough for commercial use. Early in the twentieth century most of the sulfur from both sources was simply burned off and released to the atmosphere as toxic sulfur dioxide (SO_2). A combination of necessary environmental controls plus a favorable market for native sulfur has led to recovery of abundant native sulfur from the petroleum industry. The only negative aspect of this development, however, is that sulfur production from petroleum processes fluctuates with the petroleum industry, whereas many of the operations for sulfur from salt domes are self-sufficient even if associated petroleum operations should cease.

Recovery from Metal Sulfide Mining

Sulfur from metal sulfide mining is used primarily to manufacture sulfuric acid. This sulfur is less pure than that from salt domes. Elements such as selenium (Se), arsenic (As), and tellurium (Te) which behave like sulfur in the sulfide minerals (e.g., as S^{2-} or Se^{2-}) and a few metal ions not completely removed during the metal-from-sulfur separation step following flotation are concentrated somewhat in the sulfur. Depending on the intended use of the sulfur, these elements may or may not be removed. If the sulfuric acid produced is to be used for a fungicide or insecticide in which small amounts of these trace elements are below toxic levels, the trace elements may be beneficial components. On the other hand, if a purer sulfur is required, then extensive cleanup is needed before the sulfur can be used.

Failing to properly purify sulfuric acid produced from metal sulfide mining can be dangerous. In the late 1960s, Dr. E. E. Angino and his coworkers at the Kansas Geological Survey found that the waters of the Kansas River near Lawrence, Kansas, contained relatively high amounts of arsenic. By careful investigation they were able to trace the arsenic to large masses of detergent dumped into the river, especially during its flood stage.* The cheapest (and thus most impure) sulfuric acid had been used to manufacture detergents used in large quantities at various points along the Kansas River. When sulfuric acid of a better quality was used, the arsenic levels in the river waters dropped accordingly. But this is not quite the end of the story. In the process of investigating the detergents, many commercial brands were analyzed and another problem solved. The late 1960s was the age of enzyme detergents—and it was known that some enzymes worked well, while others did not. Closer inspection disclosed that small amounts of arsenic (again due to the sulfuric acid used in preparing the detergent) were apparently killing some of the enzymes.

Unfortunately, the hazards of improperly purified sulfuric acid were not isolated soon enough. In the late 1950s several English scientists had demonstrated that arsenic found in poor-quality detergent had carcinogenic effects on workers using the detergents.† Because their work was not properly publicized, it took another decade to discover the same results and take appropriate action for quality control.

Of the remaining sources of sulfur, that available from areas of volcanic rocks is locally important in countries such as Japan, Chile, and Italy. This sulfur occurs sporadically and is relatively impure. Furthermore, miners inhale undesirable amounts of noxious fumes. Because of stricter environmental controls in the United States, native sulfur is not mined commercially and workers in areas where native sulfur occurs are monitored for toxic fume inhalation. Production and related data for sulfur are shown in Figure 5–8.

---

*E.E. Angino et al., "Arsenic in Detergents: Possible Danger and Pollution Hazard," *Science* 168 (1970): 389–90.
†J.M.A. Lenihan, H. Smith, and J.G. Chalmers, "Arsenic in Detergents," *Nature* 181 (1958): 1463–64.

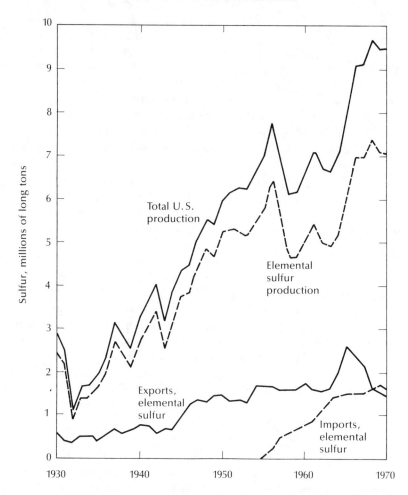

FIGURE 5–8 Sulfur production. These curves show that most U.S. production involves elemental sulfur from salt domes (recovered by the Frasch process) and by-products from the petroleum industry. As of 1975, imports roughly balance exports; that is, it is advantageous to import available high-purity sulfur when it is shipped with other commodities, while we export an equivalent amount.

Other Nonmetals

The list of nonmetals used in chemical and other industries is immense, so only a few will be mentioned here. *Halite* (NaCl) is best known as common table salt, yet this use accounts for very little of the world's halite consumption. The abundant halite available either from entrapped sea water or from evaporite deposits is used mainly for production of chlorine gas and sodium carbonate. The latter is available from nonmarine evaporite deposits, but it is cheaper to recover sodium carbonate during chlorine production.

Chlorine is the most abundant anion in sea water; estimates run as high as 250×10^{20} grams of chlorine in ocean waters. Yet, unlike bromine (which constitutes only 0.0065 percent of ocean water), chlorine must be extracted from halite. Bromine can be extracted efficiently from sea water by special chemicals, but no similar chemicals exist for chlorine.

Bromine is used in the medical field and for gasoline additives. It is one of the elements which can be cheaply and efficiently recovered from sea water. Hence, despite its limited use (relative to other nonmetals), the MACD figures for bromine are I and I (see Table 1–1) and no shortage is predicted.

Fluorine is used in steelmaking and is an important additive to some municipal drinking supplies. Unfortunately, the MACD figures are V and V for this element. Most comes from the mineral fluorite (CaF_2), which occurs in spotty fashion in vugs and vein fillings in volcanic rocks, and in pegmatites and carbonatites. When these deposits are mined for another commodity, fluorite is an important by-product. At present it is cheaper to import most of our fluorine as fluorite, but in the future we anticipate that smaller quantities of fluorite present in marine sediments and in some volcanic rocks will be more important. Fluorine is also an important by-product from processing phosphate rock. During processing F^- substitutes in appreciable quantities for OH^- in the mineral apatite and must be removed before the phosphate can be used for agriculture.

PLATE 17

Abandoned fluorite mine workings in the Zuni Mountains, New Mexico. During World War II many such mines operated, but they closed when demand fell in postwar times.

NONMETALS FOR AGRICULTURE AND THE CHEMICAL INDUSTRY

Barite (BaSO$_4$) production in the United States jumped from roughly 1.5 million tons (1.36 million metric tons) in 1945 to nearly three times that amount by 1975. The U.S. Geological Survey indicates MACD figures of II and II for identified and hypothetical resources. Barite occurs primarily in bedded sedimentary rocks, where trace amounts of barium released during mild burial and related chemical effects are fixed by SO$_4^{2-}$ in groundwaters as insoluble barite. Residual deposits and vein and cavity deposits are also locally important. Many think of barium's uses in the medical field, yet 80 percent of the barium produced is used as an additive to drilling mud because of its excellent sealing properties and resistance to temperature changes. When we remember that some 2 billion feet (600 million meters) of rock are drilled per year, we realize that barium is a valid commodity. Twenty percent of the barium produced is used in glass and ceramics, paints, electronic components, and chemicals (including those in medicine). A very important use, albeit small, is in the treatment of uranium mine tailings. When such tailings are treated with a mix of BaCl$_2$ and BaSO$_4$, radium (Ra^{2+}) is completely removed as RaSO$_4$ due to radium replacement of barium in the barite; this prevents radioactive radium from escaping into the ecosystem.

Characteristics for nonmetals used in the fertilizer and chemical industries are tabulated in Table 5–1, and Tables 5–2 and 5–3 summarize nonmetal production.

TABLE 5–1 Nonmetals for the fertilizer and chemical industries.

Nonmetal	Ore	Composition	Comments
Potassium	Sylvite	KCl	Evaporites; main potassium mineral
	Langbeinite	K$_2$Mg$_2$(SO$_4$)$_3$	Evaporites
	Carnallite	KMgCl$_3$•6H$_2$O	Evaporites
	Kainite	KCl•MgSO$_4$•3H$_2$O	Evaporites
	Polyhalite	K$_2$Ca$_2$Mg(SO$_4$)$_4$•2H$_2$O	Evaporites
Phosphorus	Apatite	Ca$_5$(PO$_4$)$_3$(F,OH)	Marine sediments; some igneous rocks
Nitrogen	Atmosphere	N$_2$(gas)	Nitrogen produced from air (80% of atmosphere is N$_2$)
	Saltpeter	NaNO$_3$	Nonmarine evaporites
	Chile saltpeter	KNO$_3$	Nonmarine evaporites
Sulfur	Native sulfur	S	Most from salt domes and petroleum processing; some from volcanic hot spring areas
	Pyrite	FeS$_2$	Poor grade; from sulfide deposits

TABLE 5–1 (continued)

Nonmetal	Ore	Composition	Comments
Chlorine	Halite	NaCl	From sea water evaporation; some from evaporites
Bromine	Bromine in sea water	Br^-	Extracted from sea water
Fluorine	Fluorite	CaF_2	Vein deposits
Barium	Barite	$BaSO_4$	Sedimentary rocks; vein deposits
Boron	Borax	$Na_2B_4O_7 \cdot 10H_2O$	Nonmarine evaporites
Sodium	Halite	NaCl	Evaporites
	Sodium sulfates and carbonates	$NaSO_4, Na_2CO_3$	Nonmarine evaporites

TABLE 5–2 Nonmetallic mineral production for agriculture and the chemical industry.

Commodity (amount produced)	1976	1977	1978
Potash (thousand mt)*	2,177	2,229	2,268
Phosphate rock (thousand mt)	44,662	47,256	49,000
Nitrogen (thousand mt)	56,900	59,200	61,400
Sulfur (thousand mt)	10,877	10,727	11,200
Salt (thousand st)*	44,191	43,412	43,680
Sodium carbonate (thousand mt)	7,560	8,040	—
Sodium sulfate (thousand st)	1,200	1,230	1,256
Boron (thousand st)	1,246	1,469	1,520
Bromine (thousand st)	230	217	208
Barite (thousand st)	1,234	1,494	1,700
Fluorspar (thousand st)	188	169	130

*mt = metric tons; st = short tons (2000 pounds)
SOURCE: U.S. Bureau of Mines, 1979.

NONMETALS FOR AGRICULTURE AND THE CHEMICAL INDUSTRY

TABLE 5–3 U. S. and world production of nonmetals for agriculture and the chemical industry (thousands of short tons unless otherwise specified).

	1975			1976		
Minerals	World Production	U. S. Production	U. S. Percent of World Production	World Production	U. S. Production	U. S. Percent of World Production
Nitrogen (agricultural)	46,722	9,341	20	48,366	10,210	21
Phosphate rock	118,254	48,816	41	117,898	49,241	42
Potash (K_2O-equivalent)	27,352	2,501	9	26,876	2,400	9
Salt	178,432	41,057	23	183,252	44,218	24
Sulfur, elemental (thousands of long tons)	49,877	11,259	23	49,741	10,706	22

SOURCE: U.S. Bureau of Mines, *Minerals Yearbook*, 1976.

Building Materials

In terms of dollar value, fossil fuels are the world's most important natural resources. Second in dollar value but first in total volume are building materials, including stone, sand and gravel, and lightweight aggregates. The U.S. Geological Survey estimates that domestic reserves of all of these are sufficient for the next twenty-five to thirty years.* In this chapter we will focus on where these resources occur and what problems we face in their production. Since the "local" transportation factor alone dictates whether production of these resources will be profitable, imports and exports of building materials are of minor importance.

Stone

Stone includes both *dimension stone* (building stone quarried and trimmed with essentially no other processing) and *crushed stone*. Of dimension stone, limestone (37%) and granite (31%) are the most common followed by sandstone (17%) and to a much lesser degree slate (8%) and marble (4%). Figure 6–1 shows the distribution of dimension stone in the United States. If we were to travel about the United States, we would see the effect of transportation on choice of building materials. For example, although granite is rugged, takes a high polish, and is a desirable dimension stone, it is prohibitively expensive to ship. Most buildings are constructed of locally available material.

Crushed stone is dominated by limestone (73%); significant mafic-igneous rocks, or traprock (10%); and granite (9%). Smaller amounts of sandstone, marble and other locally available rocks complete the list.

*U.S. Geological Survey, Professional Paper 820, 1973.

The production of dimension stone has steadily decreased during the last forty years due to development of alternate building materials such as steel-reinforced concrete. The need for crushed stone has shown continued growth [from about 100 million tons (91 million metric tons) in 1930 to 875 million tons (794 metric tons) in 1970] because substitutes for purposes such as highway and railway construction have not been found. The U.S. Geological Survey predicts only very slight increased demand for dimension stone (mainly for ornamental uses) in the next twenty to thirty years, but a 3 to 5 percent per year increased demand for crushed stone.

Sand and Gravel

We have not always considered sand and gravel as a significant industry. Yet in terms of volume it is the largest nonfuel industry in the United States. Up to now stream channels and glacial terrain have provided most of the sand and gravel, but by the year 2000 we may be forced to use such sources as marine and lake environments. In addition, extensive sand deposits off the coast of the northeastern United States are presently being dredged. The sand and gravel supply is hampered by a combination of natural distribution and poor planning during urban growth. Ideally an area should be developed so that nearby economic supplies are depleted as a city expands; then the next outlying local supply is tapped until depleted, and so forth. Unfortunately, geologic considerations and city planning rarely go hand in hand. For example, abundant sand and gravel still exist in Chicago and its suburbs. However, they are now buried under concrete and asphalt, and material must be transported from sites 50 to 60 miles (80 to 100 kilometers) away. Good examples of planning can be found in the smaller municipalities of Austin, Texas, and Albuquerque, New Mexico, where sand and gravel development has been controlled. In these cities sand and gravel operations can be overridden by city growth only when the deposits are losing their profitability. If deposits toward the interior of a city are tapped, the noise pollution, dust, and other undesirable conditions will impede production.

Lightweight Aggregates

Lightweight aggregates include such volcanic materials as pumice, scoria, cinder, and pumicite, as well as expandable clays, shale, some slate, and diatomite. (Although diatomite is suitable as a filter for many processes, very little of it is used as an aggregate.) While many of these materials are used in concretes or plasters, most are used as construction materials and

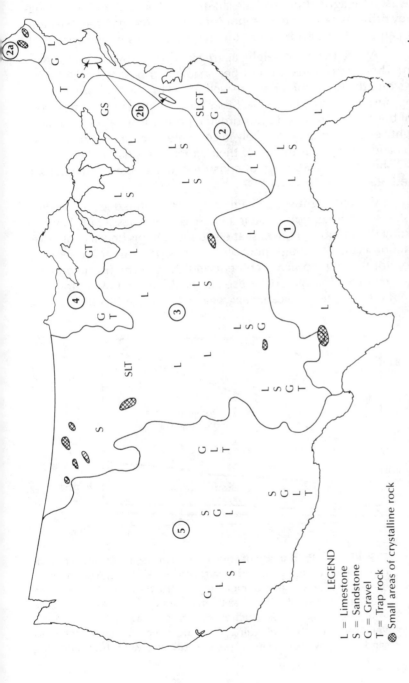

FIGURE 6-1 Distribution of dimension and crushed stone in the coterminous United States. Several provinces are identified: (1) Atlantic and Gulf Coast plain deposits; (2) Eastern crystalline belt; (2a) Northern Maine area; (2b) Triassic sandstone areas; (3) Great Plains; (4) Lake Superior area of crystalline rocks; and (5) Cordilleran, Great Basin, and Pacific coastal belt.

LEGEND

L = Limestone
S = Sandstone
G = Gravel
T = Trap rock
⊛ Small areas of crystalline rock

101

some are used for agriculture and the chemical industry. The U.S. Geological Survey projects an abundant supply of the volcanic materials well into the next century, but a shortage of the other materials by the year 2000.

All of the lightweight aggregates have several features in common: They are porous but not permeable and possess a high compressive strength. These materials are well suited for thermal and acoustic insulating purposes in ceilings and other parts of structures where conventional building materials do not provide proper insulation. Increased use of lightweight aggregates is likely in concretes for conventional building needs and to take advantage of their superior insulation properties. Figure 6–2 shows the production of construction and related materials in the United States from 1945 to 1977.

Volcanic lightweight aggregates are confined to the western United States, whereas nonvolcanic materials are widespread. Nonvolcanic mining is common to the east and south of Illinois because of lower transportation costs. Although nonvolcanic material commonly requires more monitoring (e.g., organic content and trace element mineralogic carcinogen control), this material is used in the eastern Midwest, the East, and the Southeast where volcanic aggregates are not available.

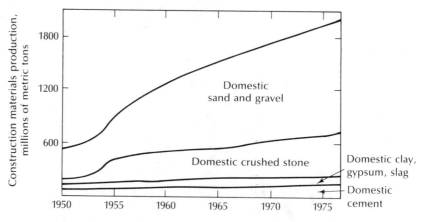

FIGURE 6–2 Production of construction materials. In terms of tonnage, only iron ore production surpasses sand and gravel. In terms of total dollar value, nonmetallic construction materials surpass even iron and steel. There has been roughly a 300 percent increase in the use of such construction materials between 1950 and 1977. Very careful urban planning must be used in development of sand and gravel deposits to prevent urban growth from affecting quarrying sites.

Clays

Clays used for industrial purposes include naturally occurring materials that contain only one clay mineral such as illite, montmorillonite, kaolinite, or halloysite. The U.S. Bureau of Mines prefers to classify clays based on the final product for which they are used, as shown in Table 6–1.

The United States is fortunate to have abundant supplies of all the clays described in Table 6–1. The production of each has risen dramatically from 1940 to 1970 with the exception of fire clay. Fire clay reached a maximum of about 10,000 tons in 1950 and declined to about 9000 (8200 metric tons) per year by 1970. All others have shown a five- to fiftyfold increase in production in the same period. Bentonite and fuller's earth will likely be consumed in greater quantities in the future due to the ever-increasing need for drilling muds. Fuller's earth is widely used in offshore drilling and in terrain that is rich in sodium. Bentonite, on the other hand, is used in low-sodium terrain. For example, using fuller's earth in a magnesium- or calcium-rich terrain would be disastrous because the sodium in fuller's earth would exchange with the magnesium or calcium of the rocks being drilled. This would cause the muds to "bind up" instead of aiding lubrication of the drilling apparatus. Similarly, bentonite is not used for offshore drilling.

TABLE 6–1   Classification of clays.

> **Kaolin** ("china clay"): Essentially pure kaolinite ideal for ceramic products.
>
> **Fire clay**: Impure kaolinite with variable amounts of organic carbon associated with it; ideal for refactory material which must be fired at high temperatures without deformation.
>
> **Bentonite and fuller's earth**: Varities of montmorillonite: Bentonite is derived from volcanic ash and contains abundant Mg; in addition, Ca is common, K less so, and Na is usually scarce. Fuller's earth, on the other hand, is typically a Na-montmorillonite. Both bentonite and fuller's earth are widely used as drilling muds although in *very* different areas.
>
> **Ball clay**: Kaolinite which contains some illite or montmorillonite; its name is derived from its plasticity, which allows it to be rolled into 30- to 50-pound (14- to 23-kilogram) balls. After firing, it is used in tiles and refactories.
>
> **Miscellaneous clay**: Illite-rich clay and shale; most consumption as fired-clay component of tiles, piping, and cement additives.

BUILDING MATERIALS

PLATE 18

Scanning electron photomicrograph showing three types of important clay minerals: (1) the pseudohexagonal booklets are kaolinite; (2) the honeycomb material is montmorillonite; and (3) the rosette material is chlorite. All three clays are common in the Morrison formation of the western United States.

Cement

By itself cement is nothing more than a fired and crushed mixture of carbonate rocks and clay minerals (or shale) moistened with water. However, once mixed with sand, gravel, or other aggregate a myriad of construction materials emerges. Portland cement, so named because of its resemblance to Portland limestone in England, is the "father" of most cements although cements date back to at least the age of the Roman Empire.

A typical feed to a kiln for preparing cement (Figure 6–3) consists of 2780 pounds (1250 kilograms) of slightly-magnesian limestone and 740 pounds (335 kilograms) of shale or clay which are first crushed and then fired at 1500°C. At this temperature carbon dioxide and water are driven off as gases. The resultant fired materials are crushed and produce about 1100 pounds (500 kilograms) of cement. Although extremely variable in composition, the shale or clay part of the feed should be selected to provide about 14 percent SiO_2, 5 to 6 percent Al_2O_3, and less than 1 percent Fe_2O_3 and impurities. Varying this composition can yield cements

PLATE 19

Limestone capping granite in the Sandia Mountains, New Mexico. The limestone contains enough shale to make it valuable for nearby cement manufacturing.

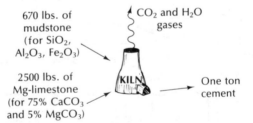

670 lbs. of mudstone (for SiO_2, Al_2O_3, Fe_2O_3)

CO_2 and H_2O gases

2500 lbs. of Mg-limestone (for 75% $CaCO_3$ and 5% $MgCO_3$)

KILN

One ton cement

FIGURE 6–3 Portland cement process. The ingredients and proportions shown here must be fairly constant for high-quality cement. Argillaceous limestones sometimes can be used directly as feed; more likely, however, fairly pure limestone must be mixed with mudstone (clay or shale) to provide the proper mix. This crushed material is roasted in a kiln at a temperature just under 1500°C. This drives off the carbon dioxide and water as gases and leaves behind a partially molten *clinker* of silicate-oxide material. When crushed to a fine size, Portland cement is the result. To produce concrete from this, sand and gravel are added.

of different strength and color. The U.S. Bureau of Mines figures for 1970 show that six countries, all highly industrialized, account for over 54 percent of cement production. The United States (at about 12 percent) was second to the Soviet Union (about 17 percent).

Concentrated efforts are made to examine argillaceous limestones in some detail because at least 20 percent contain the desired limestone-shale mix. Using these limestones would eliminate the added cost of transporting shale when the limestones are too shale-poor. Very argillaceous limestones do not fire well and contain too many impurities for good cement, yet all are examined for other potential uses. (See section on laterites in Chapter 4.)

Limestone and *dolomite* are used for fill, road cover, lightweight aggregate, and ballast as well as in cement manufacture (Figure 6–4).

Calcium Sulfates

The calcium sulfates *gypsum* ($CaSO_4 \cdot 2H_2O$) and *anhydrite* ($CaSO_4$) are common to widespread evaporite deposits. Gypsum is used to produce plaster (or plaster of Paris), which results when about 75 percent of the initial water in the gypsum is driven off. This is done by heating the gypsum to yield $2CaSO_4 \cdot H_2O$, which will in turn yield a strong binding agent when water is added. Gypsum is also used as an agent to con-

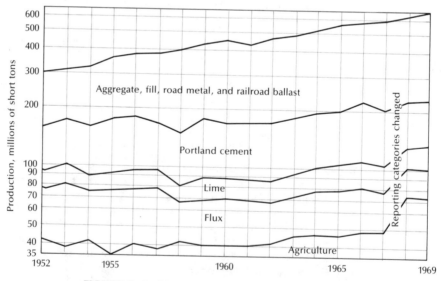

FIGURE 6–4 Uses of limestone and dolostone (dolomite). Note that the largest single use is for fill, ballast, aggregate, and road material, although increasing amounts are used for Portland cement, as lime, for fluxes in steelmaking, and for agricultural purposes.

trol setting time in cement and as a soil conditioner. Anhydrite can be used as a gypsum substitute, yet is not used often due to the abundance of gypsum.

Asbestos

Chrysotile, a hydrous magnesium silicate which occurs as acicular crystals in veins in basic and ultrabasic rocks, is the main ingredient in the material known as *asbestos*. Other hydrous magnesium, iron silicates such as tremolite, actinolite, and anthophyllite are the other ingredients. They too are present as fibrous crystals.

Asbestos used as a cement additive accounts for 70 percent of world asbestos consumption. It is also incorporated as a binding agent in insulation boards and materials and is used in corrosion-resistant reinforcing agents.

Because asbestos reserves in the United States are small, 90 percent of our needs are met by imports from Canada. The U.S. Geological Survey estimates that U.S. anthophyllite reserves are adequate as a substitute for asbestos if needed. Substitutes for asbestos are being sought because of the carcinogenic effect of asbestos minerals used in noncement construction. Links between disease and asbestos have been established, and the substance is being phased out from the production of building materials, where inhalation is likely. (See section on carcinogens in Chapter 8.)

Abrasives and Related Materials

Although the United States possesses adequate supplies of silica sand, tripoli, emery, garnet, and corundum, the hardest abrasive—diamond—is imported. However, production of artificial diamonds already supplies more than 50 percent of U.S. needs, and this percentage is likely to increase if overseas supplies become less predictable. For example, Angola, once a prime exporter of diamonds to the United States, has not done so since late 1975 after the end of Portuguese control. Although the United States is not experiencing shortages of diamond, due to its production of the artificial product, most nations *do* depend on naturally occurring material. Abrasives and their characteristics are summarized in Table 6–2, and Tables 6–3 and 6–4 describe production of building and related materials.

PLATE 20

Kimberlite boulder on top of kimberlite-rich regolith in Murfrees-boro, Arkansas. Diamonds have been recovered from this area since the early 1900s although the area is now a state park.

TABLE 6–2 Composition and use of abrasives.

Abrasive	Approximate composition	Use
Silica sand	Quartz-rich sand	Grinding, sandblasting
Tripoli	Fine-grained quartz from weathered limestone	Scouring soaps, polishing pastes
Emery	Mixture of corundum, garnet, and magnetite	In gradual disuse: some for abrasive sheeting
Garnet	Complex, cubic, anhydrous silicate	Sandblasting, lens and optical polishing, abrasive sheeting
Corundum	Al_2O_3	Some use as abrasive fine polish; largely in disuse
Diamond	Cubic native carbon	Industrial use; hardest known naturally-occurring substance (9 times harder than corundum)

PLATE 21

*Part of the Hale pegmatite quarry in Connecticut. First mined
for gem tourmaline and beryl and later for uraninite, the
abundant quartz-feldspar rock is now mined for the nearby glass
manufacturing industry in Portland-Middletown, Connecticut.*

TABLE 6–3   U. S. production of building and related materials.

Commodity (amount produced)	1976	1977	1978
Asbestos (thousand mt)*	104	93	91
Cement (thousand st)*	72,950	78,600	83,200
Clays (thousand st)	52,848	53,468	55,767
Diatomite (thousand st)	631	648	667
Gypsum (thousand st)	11,980	13,930	14,700
Lime (manufactured; st × 10³)	20,229	19,947	20,200
Perlite (thousand st)	727	871	890
Pumice (thousand st)	4,134	4,109	4,156
Sand and gravel (million st)	885	929	937
Stone (million st)	901	955	998
Talc, pyrophyllite (thousand st)	1,061	1,204	1,270

*mt = metric ton; st = short ton
SOURCE: Date from U.S. Bureau of Mines, 1979.

TABLE 6–4 U.S. and world production of building materials (thousands of short tons unless otherwise specified).

Minerals	1975			1976		
	World Prod.	U.S. Prod.	U.S. Percent of World Prod.	World Prod.	U.S. Prod.	U.S. Percent of World Prod.
Asbestos	4,564	99	2	5,566	115	2
Barite	5,358	1,318	25	5,457	1,234	23
Cement	774,277	69,721	9	811,502	74,495	9
Clay, china	15,969	5,334	33	17,029	6,115	36
Corundum	9	?	?	9	?	?
Diamond (thousand carats)	41,108	?	?	39,726	?	?
Diatomite	1,830	573	31	1,905	631	33
Feldspar	2,893	670	23	2,850	740	26
Fluorspar	5,015	140	3	4,889	188	4
Graphite	486	NA	NA	500	NA	NA
Gypsum	62,855	9,751	16	66,231	11,980	18
Lime (sold or used)	113,637	19,161	17	116,291	20,257	17
Pumice	17,059	3,907	23	17,553	4,181	24
Talc, pyrophyl-lite, soap-stone	5,385	965	18	5,944	1,092	18
Vermiculite	579	330	57	566	304	54

NA = Not applicable
? = Data not available
SOURCE: U.S. Bureau of Mines, *Minerals Yearbook*, 1976.

Energy

Energy has largely replaced *environment* as a catchword in the last decade. Whereas many publications on environment, ecology, or combined environment-ecology were published from 1967 to 1972, the number of publications on energy has far outshadowed them since 1973. The reason for this is quite simple. As the result of war in the Mideast in 1973, oil has been used by the OPEC (Overseas Petroleum Exporting Countries) nations as a weapon against the rest of the world, with considerable success. For the first time, the public has become aware of real energy problems and our reliance on oil, gas, and other petroleum products to maintain our high standard of living. Even with the reserves of the OPEC nations, petrolem product reserves will be inadequate to meet the needs of the United States—and the whole world—by early in the twenty-first century if not late in this century. Statements such as "This country has never failed to rise to any crisis to meet its needs" and reference to our development of rubber substitutes in World War II are common, and the so-called oil-marlstones are being touted as an alternative to petroleum. However, the energy picture is quite different from our World War II "rubber needs."

The United States' failure to search for alternatives to petroleum products was dramatically demonstrated when the government of Iran was overthrown in early 1979. Reduced oil production and withdrawal of direct sales to the United States led to less oil from the Mideast and forced purchase of oil from the world market at escalated prices set by OPEC. In roughly one year (August, 1978 through October, 1979) the price of gasoline at U.S. pumps rose approximately 20 percent—and this price escalation is expected to continue.

Two points also made in 1973 were (1) the United States, with less than 10 percent of the world's population, consumed roughly one-third of the energy produced in the world; and (2) the United States would have to quickly develop energy alternatives, including conservation, to offset continued reliance on imports of oil and gas, especially from OPEC nations. With regard to the first point, the implications of depleted supplies and greater energy demands outside the United States were not taken seriously by many. Addressing the second point, Dr. Dixy Lee Ray (then head of the U.S. Atomic Energy Commission) proposed an energy plan in which reliance on imports would virtually disappear between 1975 and 1980, due largely to conservation and increased domestic energy.* The sad fact is that in just four years oil imports have increased from 35 percent to over 40 percent, conservation methods have failed to provide much of an energy savings (because they are voluntary?), and the public has received little energy education. It is indeed difficult to convince many individuals of the severity of possible oil shortages. For example, when news was received that oil from Prudhoe Bay, Alaska, might be sold to Japan rather than consumed in the United States, people continued to be suspicious of domestic energy shortages.

The energy crisis is very real, especially if we remember that population, industrialization, and natural resource consumption (exclusive of petroleum products) are all increasing. Per capita consumption, in particular, is increasing. Proposed solutions to the energy crisis are numerous, but time is critical.

Oil, Gas, and Related Materials

As illustrated in Figures 7–1 and 7–2, most of the energy consumed in the United States as well as worldwide is in the form of oil, gas, or liquids produced from gas. All are commonly found together.

Petroliferous materials form from animal remains that were deposited under swamplike conditions and had accumulated over millions of years without destruction or dissemination. In brief, decaying hydrocarbon matter must be buried in special environments such as marginal-marine to nearshore-marine sedimentary basins. At a depth of about 15,000 feet (4500 meters) the temperature and pressure are sufficient for the accumulated organic matter to be *cracked*—that is, broken into new organic forms which are free to migrate from their original site. Many of these new hydrocarbons are so widely disseminated that they are of no economic significance; or else they are lost directly to the atmosphere. Many in their upward migration become caught in various struc-

*U.S. Government Printing Office, WASH–1281, 1973.

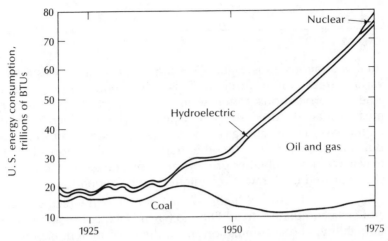

FIGURE 7–1 Energy consumption trends in the United States. Here distinction is made between domestically produced oil and gas and that provided by imports. Note that hydroelectric power has increased slightly in terms of total BTUs but decreased in percentage of total energy consumption. Total coal input has remained relatively constant, but the amount of available anthracite has decreased from about 2.5 trillion BTUs (1920) to less than 0.2 trillion BTUs (1975), which means we will rely on lower grades of coal in the future. This graph does not adequately demonstrate the input from nuclear power because it is a relatively new energy source.

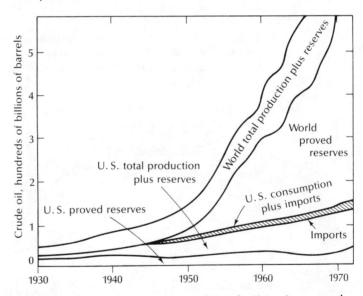

FIGURE 7–2 Crude oil reserves and production. Imports, the cross-hatched area, are increasing at an ever-expanding rate. World reserves look most favorable here, but predictions indicate that world production will peak early in the twenty-first century. U.S. production has already peaked. In short, even if the United States can afford the cost of imports, they will be insufficient to meet our demands by about the year 2010.

tural or aqueous traps. Figures 7–3 and 7–4 present a brief summary of the various traps sought in oil and gas exploration. The classical anticline, where hydrocarbons permeate upward in sandstone overlain by impermeable shale (Figure 7–4), is the type of trap from which 75 to 80 percent of the world's oil and gas have been discovered (including past production and reserves). The other traps, while often more difficult to find, may account for a higher proportion of oil and gas in the future as more sophisticated exploratory techniques are developed.

There are limits to environments in which oil can migrate and be accumulated. In addition to having favorable source rocks, migration ability, and accumulation traps, the environment explored must be relatively shallow—at least less than 10,000 feet (3000 meters) deep. At

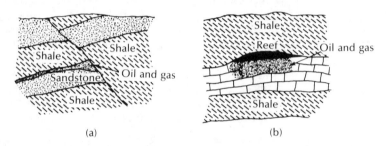

(a)   (b)

FIGURE 7–3 Two important traps for petroleum. In trap (a), a fault has allowed oil and gas to accumulate in sandstone on the footwall side of the fault where it is blocked by shale. In trap (b), a carbonate reef in a limestone layer has allowed oil and gas to accumulate.

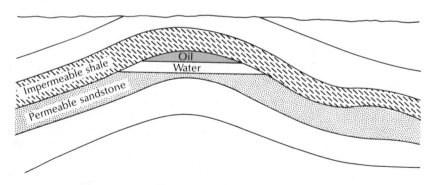

FIGURE 7–4 Structural trap for oil and gas accumulation. Almost 80 percent of the world's cumulative production and reserves are from simple structural *anticlines*. Because of their low density, oil or gas and water migrate through the permeable sandstone until further upward migration is stopped by an overlying layer of impermeable rock such as shale. Determining the structure of the subsurface by geophysical techniques maximizes the probability of drilling near the highest point of the anticline.

greater depths the petroliferous hydrocarbons are converted to other carbonaceous matter (including dissolved carbon dioxide). The age of rocks in which oil and gas are found still inspires much debate. Before the tremendous Mideast reserves were fully known in the 1950s, it was thought that a rock's oil potential decreased with increasing geologic age. This point is illustrated in Figure 7–5 and Table 7–1.

The data shown in Table 7–1 require some explanation. The 1970 figures for the United States (about 15 percent of the world total) reflect the large proportion of production and reserves from Cenozoic and Paleozoic rocks relative to Mesozoic rocks. Similarly, the tremendous Mideast reserves (more than 60 percent of the world total) are largely from Mesozoic rocks. Hence the 1970 world figures which include the Mideast (World A in Table 7–1) do not exhibit the predicted trend of smaller amounts of petroleum-producing rocks in younger geologic formations.

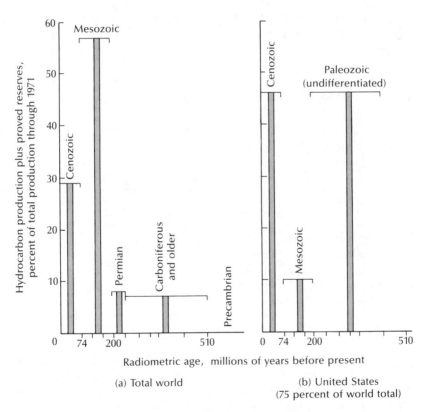

FIGURE 7–5 Age of rocks relative to oil and gas production. Most of the world's production and proved reserves comes from Mesozoic rocks, yet only 10 percent of U.S. production and reserves is from Mesozoic rocks. Thus maximum exploration in these rocks could improve U.S. oil and gas supplies.

116

TABLE 7–1 Percentage of oil production and reserves in rocks of different geologic age.

	World 1960	World A 1970	World B 1970	United States 1970
Cenozoic rocks (0–74 m.y.b.p.)	49.4	29	40	45
Mesozoic rocks (74–225 m.y.b.p.)	21.5	57	39	10
Paleozoic rocks (225–570 m.y.b.p.)	29.1	14	21	45

NOTES: 1. m.y.b.p. = millions of years before present
      2. World A includes Mideast reserves.
      3. World B exclusive of Mideast reserves.
SOURCE: Date from U.S. Geological Survey. Professional Paper 820, 1973.

In the third column of Table 7–1, 1970 world production and reserves for "giant" fields* outside the Mideast do show this trend. The total amount of oil and gas in the Mideast is unknown. Already the power of the *petrodollar* is evident, which is not surprising when we compare the figures in Table 7–2 for past production and world reserves (mostly from the Mideast) for 1971 and 1973 respectively. The data show that the United States has peaked—a fact reflected in a slight but significant decrease in production of both oil and gas between 1973 and 1974. Table 7–3 compares U.S. and world production of fossil fuels.

TABLE 7–2 Oil and gas production and reserves.

	United States	World
Oil (billions of barrels)		
Production through 1971	97	264
Reserves as of 1973	45	632
Gas (trillions of cubic feet)		
Production through 1971	415	620
Reserves as of 1973	279	1725

SOURCE: U. S. Geological Survey, Professional Paper 820, 1973.

      If we consider world oil and gas production and reserves as a function of both rock type and age, however, then we can expect additional major discoveries from the tremendous accumulations of Cenozoic and especially Mesozoic rocks on the continental shelf of the United States. For example, it is unreasonable to think that all U. S. Mesozoic deposits have been discovered, because they now represent only 10 percent of all U. S. deposits. Yet even if new discoveries from domestic

*More than one billion barrels oil and a trillion cubic feet of gas.

sources add significantly to the world supply, it is also unlikely that world supplies will be able to meet projected energy requirements; one has merely to correlate population growth with energy consumption to see that this is true. We will assume that the doubling rate for population is 33 years and speculate that the doubling rate for energy consumption, while unknown, will lessen as industrialization increases. If there is a 1:1 correlation, world oil and gas production will peak by about the year 2000 and supply will be far short of demand roughly by 2025 as shown in Figure 7–6.

Mideast oil production has increased significantly in the ten-year period from 1964 to 1974; and, based on 1974 oil demand, it is

TABLE 7–3 U. S. and world production of fossil fuels (thousands of short tons unless otherwise specified).

Minerals	1975			1976		
	World Production	U. S. Production	U. S. Percent of World Production	World Production	U. S. Production	U. S. Percent of World Production
Carbon black (million pounds)	6,937	2,742	40	7,726	3,004	39
Coal						
Bituminous	1,976,155	628,619	32	2,018,657	653,055	32
Lignite	944,677	19,819	2	985,178	25,630	3
Pennsylvania anthracite	196,301	6,203	3	196,769	6,228	3
Coke (excluding breeze)						
Gashouse	18,816	?	?	18,823	?	?
Oven and beehive	400,470	57,207	14	404,713	58,333	14
Natural gas (marketable) (million cubic feet)	47,517,774	20,108,661	42	49,459,213	19,952,438	40
Peat	223,960	772	?	222,856	969	?
Petroleum (crude) (thousand barrels)	19,497,604	3,052,048	16	21,187,147	2,971,686	14

? = Data not available
SOURCE: U.S. Bureau of Mines, *Minerals Yearbook*, 1976.

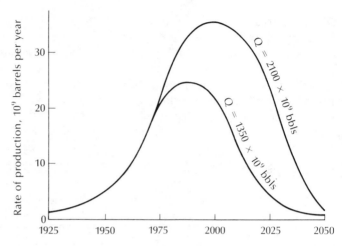

FIGURE 7–6 Cycle for world petroleum production. This graph shows two values for quantity (Q) of petroleum products. For $Q = 1350$ billion barrels, 80 percent of the total will be used by the year 2003 (to peak at 1990); while for $Q = 2100$ billion barrels, 80 percent of the total will be used by the year 2032 (to peak at 2000). These estimates have been made by experts from several federal and state agencies, the National Academy of Sciences, and acknowledged experts in industry. The world will have very limited supplies of petroleum products by the mid-twenty-first century. (After M. K. Hubbert, reproduced from *Resources and Man*, 1969, with the permission of the National Academy of Sciences, Washington, D.C., and M. K. Hubbert.)

clear that the United States is nowhere near self-reliance. (Remember that imports have increased from 35 percent in 1973 to 42 percent in 1977—an alarming 20 percent jump.) How the United States uses its petroleum products is illustrated in Table 7–4.

From the data in Table 7–4 several items are noteworthy. First, the United States has so far been unsuccessful in attempts to find an economical substitute for oil and gas in transportation. Although liquid fuel suitable for some engines has been produced from coal on a limited scale, it is not competitive in terms of supply or cost. While roughly 30 percent of total energy requirements are for transportation, oil and gas represent 77 percent of the petroleum products consumed in household and commercial use and 69 percent of that consumed in industrial use; so it is in these areas that substitutes for oil and gas can and must be found. Energy is not a luxury anymore—it is a necessity. Second, electrical energy can probably offset oil and gas requirements more easily than energy from coal; and the United States *does* have the potential for dramatically increasing its electrical energy output. Equally important are conservation measures for petroleum products, not only in the transportation industry but in nontransportation uses as well. The U.S. conservation effort has

TABLE 7–4   U. S. use of petroleum products.

Household and Commercial Use (30% of total)		Industrial Use (40% of total)
Natural gas	43%	44%
Oil	34%	25%
Electricity	21%	11%
Coal	2%	18%
Other	—	2%
Transportation Use (30% of total)		
Oil and gas	96%	
Other	4%	

SOURCE: U. S. Bureau of Mines, *Minerals Yearbook*, 1974.

largely been restricted to federal and state buildings, with mandatory thermostat settings to minimize energy consumption. Mass transit systems are not yet operating in many metropolitan areas, and, even where contemplated or under construction, they may be inadequate to reduce petroleum product consumption effectively. To date, carpools have had only limited success and voluntary energy conservation has failed. Dr. Dixy Lee Ray's optimistic hope that petroleum imports could be cut to almost zero by 1980 has not materialized.

In summary, there is some basis for optimism that new oil and gas will be found in the United States. From the end of 1973 to the end of 1974, the number of oil wells increased from 497,378 to 497,631.* Use of our dwindling overall reserves and energy use patterns must be drastically modified to meet just our transportation needs!

The next several figures illustrate petroleum product patterns in the United States and worldwide. Figure 7–7 strikingly shows that the total new supply indeed peaked at about 1974; this is true even though new oil from Alaska in the late 1970s resulted in somewhat of an oil glut in the western United States. However, these data are misleading as our imports increased significantly during this period.

Figure 7–8 shows the curves for domestic production. Note that in both Texas and Louisiana, the two principal producers in the United States, production started to decline in the early 1970s.

Worldwide distribution of oil between 1964 and 1974 is shown in Figures 7–9 and 7–10. The U.S. production has fallen from 27.0 percent in 1964 to 15.6 percent in 1974, and the trend continues. Middle Eastern production increased in the same period from 27.0 percent to 38.8 percent. Remember that these data are based on production, not on

*U. S. Bureau of Mines, *Minerals Yearbook*, 1974.

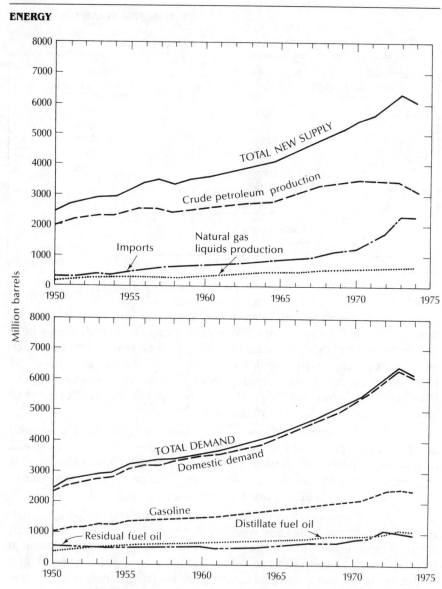

FIGURE 7–7 Supply and demand for oil in the United States. Although they dropped slightly in 1975, the demand curves have continued to escalate and domestic supply has continued to drop. (From U.S. Bureau of Mines, *Minerals Yearbook*, 1974.)

reserves. When reserves are counted, the difference between the Middle East and the United States is even more striking. This is illustrated in part by the oil flow pattern illustrated in Figure 7–11. For political reasons or because of increased European demand, oil flow to the United States

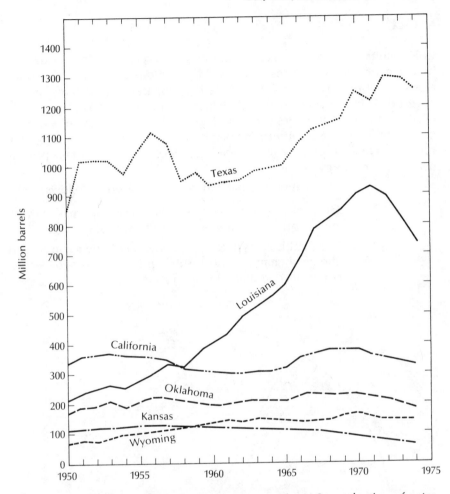

FIGURE 7–8 Oil-producing states. The U.S. production of petro-leum has already peaked. Production in Texas and Louisiana has dropped noticeably, and a steady decline is also noted for Califor-nia, Oklahoma, and Kansas. Only Wyoming shows a slight increase after 1972. (From U.S. Bureau of Mines, *Minerals Yearbook*, 1974.)

could at any time be shut off from the Middle East. This is supported by the 1974 daily demand figures for petroleum shown in Figure 7–12.

The price of oil and gas has spurred well drilling in the 1970s (Figure 7–13), even though the world is faced with diminishing reserves. Sophisticated techniques have led to success on a number of ventures, yet the number of dry wells still about equals the number of producing oil wells (see Figure 7–13).

Coal

Coal results from the slow accumulation of dead plant material, usually in brackish nonmarine basins. The world distribution of coals of various types is shown in Figure 7–14. While it is apparent that a large area is covered, it is also noteworthy that most of the world's coal resources occur in the Northern Hemisphere. Hence if industrialization is to proceed rapidly in the Southern Hemisphere, coal use must be budgeted carefully. For example, use in developing a steel industry may take priority over use for energy needs.

The formation of coal can be summarized as follows:

1. Dead plant matter accumulates in swampy areas to eventually form *peat* (10% solids, 90% water).

2. The peat is compacted and dehydrated due to burial and chemical changes and forms *lignite*, the immediate precursor to combustible coal forms.

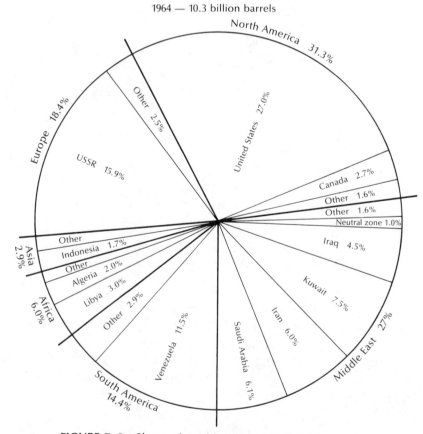

1964 — 10.3 billion barrels

FIGURE 7–9 Share of world crude oil production in 1964. (From U.S. Bureau of Mines, *Minerals Yearbook*, 1974.)

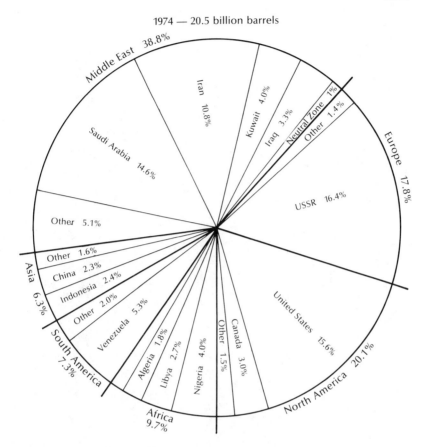

1974 — 20.5 billion barrels

FIGURE 7–10 Share of world crude oil production in 1974. (From U.S. Bureau of Mines, *Minerals Yearbook*, 1974.)

3. Continued burial of the lignite causes very low-grade metamorphism, and the lignite is converted to *subbituminous coal*.

4. Pressure and temperature increase to form *bituminous coal*.

5. Pressure and temperature continue to increase to form *anthracite*.

Once anthracite has been formed, further increases in temperature and pressure so hardens the carbonaceous matter that it loses its combustible value and eventually forms graphite. The original carbonaceous matter deposited is very impure, so the resulting coal varies widely in characteristics such as moisture content and caloric (heat) value. A simple ranking of various types of coal, including lignite, is given in Table 7–5.

Although the data in Table 7–5 are subject to uncertainties, moisture content generally decreases with increasing rank of coal, while

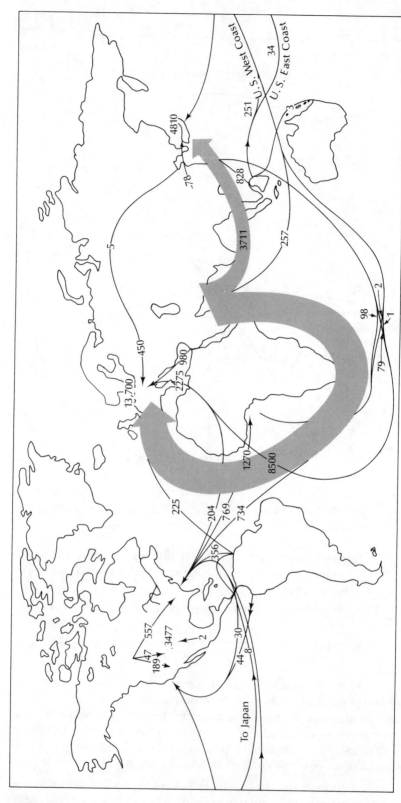

FIGURE 7–11 Movement of crude oil to major consumers is dominated by shipments from the Mideast. (From U.S. Bureau of Mines, Division of Petroleum and Natural Gas, June 1975.)

DAILY PETROLEUM DEMAND
56.0 million barrels

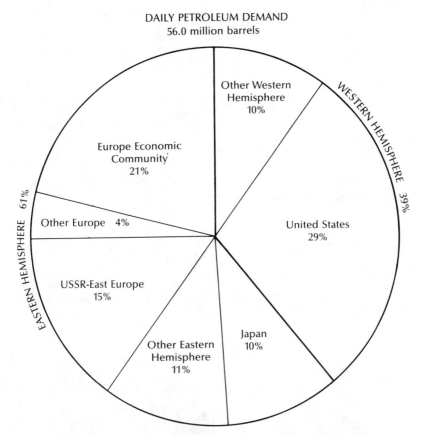

FIGURE 7–12 World daily petroleum demand in 1974. The reliance of the United States on petroleum is very obvious here; Japan's need for petroleum is also noteworthy. (From U.S. Bureau of Mines, *Minerals Yearbook*, 1974.)

fixed carbon and approximate heat value increase. Volatile matter, however, first increases and then decreases. Thus many coals will not burn cleanly because sulfur in the volatile matter is emitted in gaseous form during combustion. Anthracites are the cleanest coals, but they actually start to decrease in heat value at their highest grade due to metamor-

TABLE 7–5 Various types of coal.

Type of Coal	Approximate Heat Value (BTUs)	Volatile Matter	Moisture Content	Fixed Carbon
Lignite	7,000	25%	45%	25%
Subbituminous	10,000	35%	25%	45%
Bituminous	14,500	35%	10%	55%
Anthracite	14,500	8%	4%	90%

SOURCE: U.S. Geological Survey, Professional Paper 820, 1973.

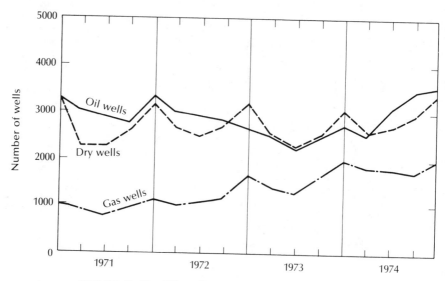

FIGURE 7–13 Oil and gas wells drilled in the United States (by quarter) from 1971 to 1974. (U.S. Bureau of Mines, *Minerals Yearbook*, 1974.)

PLATE 22

Coal carrier about to leave dock at Sault Ste. Marie, Michigan. (Courtesy of W. E. Elston.)

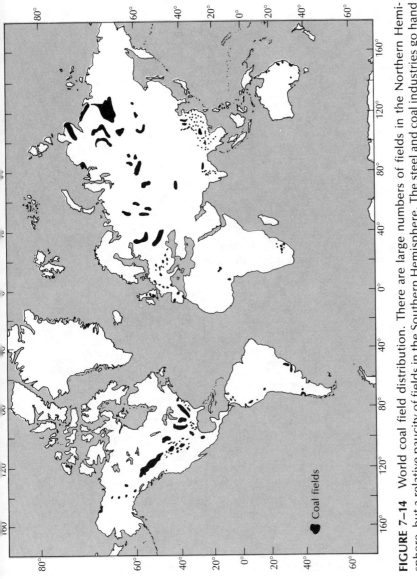

FIGURE 7–14 World coal field distribution. There are large numbers of fields in the Northern Hemisphere, but a relative paucity of fields in the Southern Hemisphere. The steel and coal industries go hand in hand, so it is easy to see why there is little coal production in "third world" nations. In addition, even when iron ore is available in the Southern Hemisphere (with the exception of South Africa), coal is lacking. Thus the iron ore must be shipped to where coal and limestone are available.

Coal fields

phism. Such *meta-anthracite* should ideally be saved for the steel industry and not used for fuel because it has excellent coking coal qualities but produces less heat than lower grades of anthracite and the highest grades of bituminous coals.

Variation in the trace element content of coals must be monitored before they are marketed. Coal is enriched not only in radioactive uranium, thorium, and radium, but often contains high concentrations of selenium, beryllium, arsenic, molybdenum, zinc, cadmium, mercury, lead, chromium, and other elements, which can be carcinogenic (see Chapter 8).

Although coal resources are enormous, coal resource development may present more problems than solutions. First, most future coal resources will require large-scale stripping operations. The costs of land reclamation may be excessive where the coal occurs in thin layers with thin soil and rock cover. Coal exposed at the surface is easily oxidized and loses its caloric potential. Second, the coal industry—not anticipating oil and gas shortages or possible slowdown of nuclear energy development—did not carry out necessary development work (including training personnel and upgrading equipment) during the 1960s and early 1970s and thus was unprepared for short-term solutions to energy problems after 1973. Third, clean coal is scarce; and the burning of lower-grade coal yields many more carcinogens (including radioactive species!) than does uranium mining, milling, and processing.* Coal gasification (i.e., production of clean methane gas from coal *in situ*) is only in the development stage and still leaves the problem of energy (or power) transmission. The largest deposits of low-grade coals are simply located too far from the population centers that need the energy.

The U.S. Geological Survey estimates U.S. coal reserves at 3 trillion tons, of which about half could be recovered to provide some 38×10^{15} BTUs. This would be roughly enough heat to meet U.S. energy needs for 190 years—*if* energy consumption levels off by the year 2000, and *if* coal can be used for generation of electricity and as a substitute for other forms of energy. This is unlikely, however. About 70 percent of domestic coals, with low sulfur content, occur *west* of the Mississippi River; but more than 55 percent of the caloric value is locked up in high-sulfur coals *east* of the Mississippi. Coal gasification and conversion are needed to exploit the low-grade coals.

Coal gasification can be achieved as follows:

1. For each pound (0.5 kilogram) of coal, combustion takes place in the presence of approximately 12 pounds (5.5 kilograms) of air and yields *stack gas* (CO_2, H_2O, N_2, and others.)

---

*See B. Cohen, "The Disposal of Radioactive Wastes From Fission Reactors," *Scientific American* (June 1977): 21-31, for a lucid discussion of this problem.

2. The stack gas produced is then used for combustion of another pound of coal in the presence of 6 pounds (2.7 kilograms) of air. This step of air gasification yields *power gas* (CO, H_2, and N_2).

3. Power gas is actually a lean fuel-gas with about one-sixth the caloric value of natural gas.

4. Power gas cannot be used as pipeline-quality natural gas, but it can be used for (a) generation of electricity; (b) industrial heating; and (c) other applications such as drying of grain. Remember that 40 percent of industrial needs is for space heating, in which power gas would be an adequate substitute for fuel oil, natural gas, or electricity.

Coal conversion plants produce *synthetic natural gas* (SNG). Seven plants are planned for completion by 1981, and tentative plans call for an additional 4 to 5 per year to be built through 1985 for a total of 26. To operate these plants, the coal is strip mined, gasified, purified, and fed to *magnetohydrodynamic generators*.

Thus we can see that coal can be used as a substitute for organic compounds and derivatives now produced from petroliferous products and for production of synthetic fuels—and as a combustible fuel.

Nuclear Energy: From Rocks to Reactors

Nuclear energy has provoked heated debate during the past decade. Advocates of nuclear energy point out its potential in terms of benefits to land reclamation. Since one gram of uranium can yield as much energy as 2270 kilograms of coal, then producing fuel for nuclear energy would cause fewer mining scars on the earth's surface. Potentially recoverable coal amounts to 1.5 trillion metric tons from which we could obtain energy to meet domestic needs for some 190 years. To recover this amount of coal, however, would require stripping lands (including both mined coal and overburden) roughly equivalent to the combined areas of North and South Dakota! Considering the poor record for land reclamation by the coal mining industry (about one-third at best), the pollutants (including more radioactive material per uranium-fuel equivalent per ton), and the effects on urban life, it is probable that this total amount of coal will *not* be mined to meet our needs.* For comparison, a 1000-megawatt nuclear reactor requires about 200 metric tons of uranium per year, whereas a

*One hope is that development of *in situ* coal conversion may eliminate much of the strip mining.

coal-fired generating plant of the same capacity requires 2 million metric tons of coal. Coal mining affects 400,000 times more land than does uranium mining. Furthermore, most coal will continue to be strip-mined, but underground mining of uranium ore will be increased. Thus, even less land will have to be reclaimed from uranium mining.

Types of Reactors

Uranium resources for the United States are probably adequate to supply the nuclear reactors that are planned up to the year 2000; that is, we have uranium ore containing about 2 million tons of U_3O_8. The U.S. Department of Energy projections base nuclear energy need on 60 percent of electrical utilities' needs, which amount to 20 percent of our total energy consumption.

The picture is not so optimistic for the twenty-first century. Even with uranium available from outside the United States (especially from Canada and Australia, where recent discoveries have been made), the need for increased electrical output will require construction of more light-water reactors* (LWRs)—and the cost of construction is increasing drastically. Despite uranium's advantages over coal, it is still desirable to mine, mill, and process as little uranium as possible. The U.S. government initially intended to use LWRs as only a short-term way of meeting world energy needs until fast-breeder reactors (FBRs) were developed. The LWRs use uranium-235 enriched fuel, but 99.3 percent of natural uranium mined is the isotope uranium-238, which is not fissionable.

In converter reactors (CRs) a fuel mix of roughly 65 percent 235-enriched uranium is mixed with thorium-232, the only isotope of thorium found in nature. Enough fast neutrons are produced so that uranium-233 is made from thorium-232 with the production of more neutrons to, in part, breed the process. The uranium-233 is, like uranium-235, an excellent reactor fuel. Processing thorium is expensive, and CRs are intended as stopgap measures until breeder reactors are put into use.

The fast-breeder reactors use uranium-238, which, when bombarded with fast neutrons, forms plutonium-239. The plutonium-239 not only fissions (like uranium-235) but also produces more neutrons, which in turn create more plutonium-239 from uranium-238, and so on. This type of reactor actually *breeds* more fuel than is consumed, hence its name. Furthermore, since uranium-238 is the isotope most important for the FBRs, this means that less than 1/100 of the amount of fuel for LWRs is needed for FBRs. Remembering that 2 million tons (1.8 million metric

*References on types of reactors and how they operate are given in the bibliography.

tons) of coal are needed as fuel for a 1000-megawatt generating plant and 200 tons (180 metric tons) of uranium ore for an equivalent LWR plant, note that the amount of uranium ore needed for an FBR plant of the same capacity is only 1.4 tons.*

If the decision to use FBRs is made on schedule (1988, according to U. S. Department of Energy), then there is a sufficient uranium ore supply for virtually thousands of years. If the decision is postponed to 1991, then the LWR requirements for uranium will not be eased until about the year 2015—and our uranium resources will be stretched very thin. You may ask, "Why the delay?" The answer is quite simple: plutonium. The FBRs create plutonium, which is one of the most toxic substances known. Yet from our knowledge of Oklo and our use of reactors, we know that plutonium not only can but is being safely handled.

If and when the FBRs are in use with LWRs by the year 2000, the United States will have achieved a great step toward energy self-reliance. Important aspects of the nuclear fuel cycle, the fission and breeding processes, and fuel demands based on LWRs or FBRs are shown in Figures 7–15, 7–16, 7–17, and 7–18.

Mining: Ore containing 0.05% to 1.0% U_3O_8

Milling: Uranium content increased to 80%

Conversion: Uranium converted to gaseous UF_6

Enrichment: U-235 enriched from 0.7% to 3.2%

Fuel Rod Fabrication: U-235 enriched fuel rods manufactured

Reactor: Fuel rods used for electrical energy production

FIGURE 7–15 Uranium for reactors. In this simplified flow diagram, low-grade ore (0.05 to 1.0% U_3O_8) is milled to produce yellowcake (oxidized uranium compounds containing 90 to 95% U_3O_8); and the tailings are carefully separated and monitored. Vanadium and molybdenum are recovered as by-products during the milling process. The yellowcake is then shipped to conversion plants and converted to gaseous UF_6, which is then treated in diffusion plants to increase the U-235 content from 0.7 percent (normal ore) to about 3 to 4 percent U-235 (enriched ore)—a product that will sustain fission reactions. The enriched uranium (3–4% U-235; 96–97% U-238) is then used to fabricate fuel rods for use in nuclear reactors. The heat generated when the U-235 fissions in the enriched rods is sufficient to operate an electrical power plant. About 7 tons of normal uranium ore is equivalent to 25,000 tons (22,700 metric tons) of medium-grade coal (for the generation of an equivalent amount of energy).

*U.S. Atomic Energy Commission, 1974.

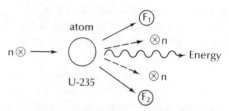

FIGURE 7–16 Nuclear fission. In nuclear fission, an atom of U-235 is struck by a neutron and then fissions into two fragments (F_1 and F_2), producing additional neutrons and energy. The energy generated by the nuclear process is used to heat water, which passes through a heat exchanger to produce steam. The steam then turns a turbine to generate electricity.

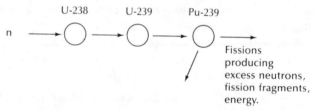

FIGURE 7–17 Breeding uranium-238. In a conventional light-water reactor the neutrons affect only atoms of U-235, which constitute only some 3 to 4 percent of the total uranium. The U-238 (96–97% of the total) is unaffected in the light-water reactor processes. When fast neutrons are used, however, U-238 produces Pu-239 (plutonium). Not only does Pu-239 fission, but it also produces more neutrons which strike other atoms of U-238; thus plutonium *breeds* more fuel.

Uranium

Prior to World War II, uranium was used primarily as a source for radium (used in the production of luminescent paints). Uraninite (UO_2) and other uranium-bearing minerals from pegmatites were the main supply of uranium. With the coming of the atomic age in 1945, demand for uranium skyrocketed and the small production of uranium from pegmatites was dwarfed by uranium from other sources.

Over 95 percent of the world's reserves of uranium ore is in sedimentary or metasedimentary rocks. In the United States, 95 percent is obtained from so-called sandstone types of uranium-bearing deposits of the Phanerozoic Age. In rocks of the Precambrian Age, mainly outside the United States, original sedimentary deposits have been reworked (i.e., chemically or mechanically redeposited) and now exist as metamorphosed quartz-pebble conglomerate or vein deposits. Veins in

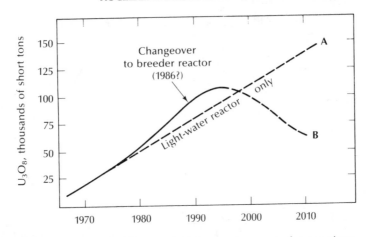

FIGURE 7–18 Projected annual U.S. requirements for uranium. The United States will probably have about 200 nuclear-fired power plants on-line by the year 2000. If only the light-water reactor is used (curve **A**), then the yearly demand will increase; in this case domestic reserves will barely meet predicted demand by 2000. If the breeder reactor becomes operational in 1986, then less uranium will be required (curve **B**); in this case domestic uranium reserves will be adequate. At this time, however, the fate of the breeder reactor is uncertain in the United States even though it is already in use in several other countries (France, United Kingdom, and the Soviet Union).

igneous rocks account for minor production. A future resource is the large, pegmatitic- and porphyritic-granite of Namibia (South-West Africa) known as the Rossing Deposit. This unique deposit contains a relatively high concentration of finely disseminated uraninite and was opened to pit mining in 1979. The Rossing Deposit opens the possibility of finding other such deposits in igneous rocks.

In a sandstone-type deposit, uranium is presumably formed in the following fashion. First, the source region for the uranium is thought to be well removed from the eventual site of deposition. As rocks weather, the major rock-forming elements behave differently than many trace elements, as shown in Table 7–6. Note that the trace elements uranium, vanadium, selenium, and molybdenum are not only oxidized during weathering but also tend to form complexes (usually as oxy-anions such as VO_4^{3-}); thus they tend to be removed as a group from more insoluble elements such as aluminum and Fe^{3+}.

In the second part of the uranium deposit formation we assume that solutions bearing uranium, vanadium, selenium, and molybdenum percolate through permeable sandstone more readily than

TABLE 7–6   Effects of weathering on elements.

Element	Valence in Unweathered Rock	Valence in Solution	Relative Solubility
Si	4+	4+	High, as H_4SiO_4
Al	3+	3+	Low; precipitates as $Al(OH)_3$
Fe	2+, 3+	2+, 3+	2+ species soluble; 3+ species insoluble
K	1+	1+	High
Na	1+	1+	High
Mg	2+	2+	High
Ca	2+	2+	High
U	4+	6+	Soluble as complex
V	2+, 3+	5+	Soluble as complex
Se	2−	6+	Soluble as complex
Mo	4+	6+	Soluble as complex

through over- and underlying shales. When carbonaceous matter or other reductants are encountered, the uranium, vanadium, selenium, and molybdenum are reduced and precipitate out as newly formed minerals in the sandstone. The major rock-forming elements present (K, Na, Mg, Ca, and Si) are unaffected by oxidation-reduction reactions and continue to percolate further into the sandstone. Thus commonly we find not only uranium enriched at the interface between oxidized, hematite-bearing sandstone and reduced, pyrite-bearing sandstone, but vanadium, selenium, and molybdenum are enriched as well.

In the United States, sandstone-type deposits are found in the nonmarine sedimentary basins of Wyoming, the Colorado Plateau, and coastal Texas (Figure 7–19). Well over 50 percent of U.S. uranium reserves are located in New Mexico in the Grants Mineral Belt; and 25 percent of world reserves are in the Grants Mineral Belt. These deposits are present in rocks from near the surface (e.g., the world's largest open-pit uranium mine is the Jackpile-Paguate Pit located near Laguna, New Mexico) and at the depths of thousands of feet (e.g., the mines of the Ambrosia Lake District near Grants, New Mexico). The deposits in Wyoming and Texas are located close to the surface and can be mined by open-pit methods. In Texas some deposits are considered too low-grade to be economically mined even by open-pit methods, hence *solution mining* is now being tried. In this method several wells are drilled into an ore-bearing horizon. One or more of these are injection wells into which either an acidic or alkaline solution capable of dissolving uranium is introduced. The remainder of the wells are recovery wells, into which the dissolved uranium is pumped (see Figure 2–4). This method of min-

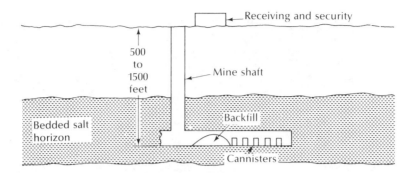

FIGURE 7–19 Radioactive waste disposal in bedded salt deposits. One of the most popular proposed methods for the radioactive waste disposal is to use bedded salt horizons in areas where seismic activity is low and volcanism is absent. The salt's very existence precludes the passage of large amounts of water through the strata (or the salts would have dissolved), and heat from the radioactive waste will anneal any cracks in the salts. Such storage sites are now being investigated in New Mexico, Michigan, and New York.

PLATE 23

High-grade uranium ore associated with clay (dark areas) and organic matter at an underground mine in the Grants Mineral Belt, New Mexico. The scale is indicated by the miner's hard hat in the bottom right-hand corner. It is concentrations of ore pods such as this that the explorer tries to find by drilling from the surface some 600 to 4500 feet (180 to 1370 meters) above!

135

PLATE 24

Underground uranium ore from a mine in the Laguna District, New Mexico. This ore, which consists of dark uranium minerals mixed with organic matter, is called "rod ore" because it has seeped downward across bedding planes of the host sandstone. The scale is indicated by the rock hammer.

ing uranium has great potential because not only can low-grade deposits be mined, but also many of the environmental problems associated with open-pit and underground mining are avoided. Unknown, however, are the possibility of subsidence due to minerals being dissolved and the possibility of dissolved substances being transported into nearby urban water supplies. For these reasons, work in this area is proceeding cautiously.

Elsewhere in the world many uranium deposits are found in Precambrian rocks, often as metamorphosed placers and other sedimentary rocks. While typically smaller and more difficult to locate, they are usually more uranium-rich and easier to mine. An interesting deposit is the uranium-gold Witwatersrand placer deposit of South Africa. Both uraninite and native gold are recovered from a metamorphosed placer deposit; mining the gold allows economic recovery of uranium.

Future resources include deposits of very low grade uranium-bearing black shales and other rocks. A practical method of recovering uranium from these rocks without causing environmental problems has not been developed, however.

Pros and Cons of Nuclear Power

Those who protest the use of nuclear power fear several dangers from this energy source, including:

1. Atomic explosions from reactors (impossible from reactor design).

2. Health hazards due to radiation near reactors (about the same increase if one moved from New York to Denver because of increased radiation with increasing altitude).

3. Theft or sabotage of nuclear materials and facilities (considered by "nukes"* to be virtually impossible in the United States).

4. Damage to the environment from heated water used as a coolant. (This can be, and is, prevented by cooling towers where necessary; elsewhere the heat so dispersed may actually be beneficial).

5. Core meltdown due to failure of fail-safe monitoring, resulting in a nonnuclear explosion that would release radioactive gas to the atmosphere. (This could only occur if cladding facilities were absent, and they are not).

6. Inadequate storage of radioactive waste. (Ways to store waste are known, but political factors prevent the implementation of several plans.)

The comments in parentheses in this list are used by nuclear power advocates to counter these statements.

Risk assessment of conventional and nonconventional energy sources is a relatively new field of research. In order of *increasing risk per energy type*, various sources are ranked as follows:[†]

1. Natural gas (safest)

2. Nuclear

3. Ocean thermal**

4. Hydroelectric

5. Solar space-heating

6. Methanol

---

*"Nukes" is the popular word for nuclear energy advocates.

[†]H. Inhaber, "Risk with Energy from Conventional and Non-conventional Sources," *Science* 203 (1979): 718-23.

**Data from projections based on available 1978 data.

7. Wind power*
8. Solar-thermal*
9. Solar-photovoltaic*
10. Oil
11. Coal (least safe)

Total labor-days lost for natural gas and nuclear are, respectively, 8 and 10; *combined* solar (space heating, thermal, photovoltaic), 2200; oil, 2500; and coal, 2900. Inhaber concludes that:

> The large differences in risk between many of the energy systems discussed make it likely that, while the absolute values of labor-days lost per unit energy will probably change in the future, the relative rankings of the systems will not change substantially. Only time and a deeper understanding of these systems can verify this contention.[†]

To many, the fact that combined solar sources do indeed involve relatively high risk may come as a surprise; but when we consider the large quantities of metals necessary for construction of solar units, possibly carcinogenic materials used in photovoltaic cells, and other factors detailed in Inhaber's report, the assignment of a relatively high risk based on 1978–79 technology is quite realistic.

Another positive aspect of nuclear energy is as follows: Since heat is produced by radiation, the usual airborne gases and particulate matter associated with coal-fired plants are absent. Nuclear fuel is truly a clean fuel.

Radioactive Waste

In the fission process not only is intense radiation released but many of the waste products are radioactive as well. While these waste products initially build up in nuclear fuel rods, they are eventually removed, condensed, and stored in temporary facilities until agreement is reached for a safe, permanent repository, usually in geologic sites. When comparing "fuel-equivalent" per "fuel-equivalent" for coal versus uranium, it has been shown that coal releases more radioactivity (plus large amounts of other carcinogens) to the environment.** Yet the argument against possible geologic repositories is, "How do we know that a repository will be safe for 250,000 years?" This figure is commonly being used due to the small amount of plutonium-239 contained, which has a half-life of some

---

*Data from projections based on available 1978 data.
†Inhaber, op. cit., p. 723.
**Cohen, op. cit.

24,000 years—and the rule of thumb is that radioactive waste must be stored for ten times its half-life to be rendered safe.

Many geologic sites have been proposed for storage of radioactive waste. Waste can be condensed to very small quantities; for example, by the year 2000 the space required for such waste will be about the size of a football field for areal coverage, assuming current nuclear reactor growth. Some of the sites being considered are

1. Deep-sea bed disposal.
2. Storage in the Antarctic.
3. Storage in bedded salt deposits.
4. Storage in crystalline basement rocks.
5. Storage in shales.
6. Others—including rocket disposal in space.

Of these, storage in bedded salt deposits has received considerable attention. Bedded salts are, by definition, very dry or else they would dissolve. Thus if we select a site in a bedded salt (Figure 7–19) in an area of low earthquake probability, great tectonic stability, and low urban development, then we would have an almost ideal site. In fact, the U.S. government plans pilot storage in such sites within the next decade. Not all countries with a present or anticipated nuclear technology have access to bedded salt deposits, hence research in the other areas continues. Japan, for example, is part of a volcanic-island-arc system which is tectonically unstable. Thus storage in granite or deep-sea beds is being considered for Japan's nuclear waste. With increasing trade with the People's Republic of China, short transport and land storage of Japan's nuclear waste is a possibility.

Deep-sea repositories are being researched at some length, yet this is perhaps the least desirable type of storage because we know the least about how containers behave in such an environment. For example, can we unequivocally state that there would be no radioactive waste lost to the sea over 250,000 years? This is perhaps impossible to answer.

Waste storage in the Antarctic is at first glance somewhat attractive because of its low population density, but it would be necessary to change international policy forbidding disposal of radioactive waste there. Furthermore, the Antarctic may not be geologically suitable; that is, we are less certain about tectonic stability and the significance of volcanogenic transport there than in anywhere else in the world.

Repositories in crystalline rocks are being considered by the United States, Sweden, Japan, Canada, France, and other countries, yet we do not have sufficient knowledge of basement rock technology. For example, many crystalline basement rocks are fractured, even in tectoni-

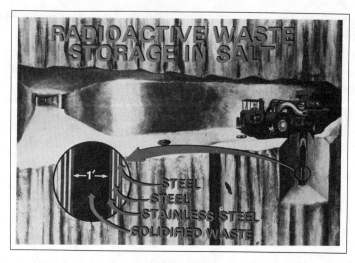

PLATE 25

Cutaway sketch of a possible radioactive waste storage facility in bedded salt. The very small dimensions of the waste cannisters are shown in the inset.

cally stable areas. Have these fractures resulted from relatively recent events or are they very old (i.e., safe)? Until this question can be adequately answered, crystalline rocks will remain problematic.

Some 70 percent of the sedimentary cover, which makes up 75 percent of the continental earth, is shale; yet this common sedimentary rock is only now receiving due consideration for waste storage. Part of the procrastination in shale research comes from an initial commitment to bedded salts and to igneous rocks; and part is due to uncertainties about clay minerals which constitute shales. That is, we are unsure whether these minerals are adequate to retain radioactive elements if they escape waste cannisters.

To explore the feasibility of shale, let us briefly comment on the information gained from studying the Oklo uranium mine in Gabon.* The uranium at this site was deposited soon after sedimentation some 2.0 billion years ago at a time when the amount of uranium-235 in total uranium was 3.16 percent—just about the value to which uranium-235 is enriched today. Due to a combination of high initial concentration of uranium, high uranium-235 content, a proper amount of water, and a lack of neutron-absorbing elements, the uranium deposited in shale-filling fracture zones sustained a fission chain reaction for some 500,000 years and produced over 10,000 megawatt-years of energy! Ore mined from

---

*G.A. Cowan, "A Natural Fission Reactor," *Scientific American* (June 1976): 36–47.

these zones at Oklo is depleted in uranium-235 to about one-half or less of the 0.7 percent in normal uranium. Some Oklo ores contain less than 0.3 percent uranium-235! We do not know of any other ways in which uranium-235 can be depleted other than by nuclear fission. Furthermore, the stable products formed after decay of the radioactive fission products are found at Oklo as well as small amounts of plutonium and neptunium. When we compare a hypothetical fission-yield curve for uranium-235 fission, measurements made from Oklo ores, and the normal crustal abundance of elements in the same atomic mass range, they are in remarkable agreement.* The Oklo "reactor" ores yield isotopic patterns for many elements which are identical to isotopic fission-yield laboratory experiments; whereas low grade, normal ore yields isotopic patterns for the same elements which are typical of all the rest of the earth's crust. Thus nature "beat" people in developing a nuclear reactor by some 2.0 billion years.

More important, however, is that most of the fission products remained in place during and after the reactor's lifetime. This 2.0-billion-year experiment convincingly demonstrates that the Oklo site, an impure shale, is suitable for all forms of nuclear waste except the gases krypton and xenon. Where some migration has occurred, it is local and in terms of years—250,000 versus 1,800,000,000—unimportant. Thus Oklo also illustrates that shales in a tectonically stable environment are indeed suitable for radioactive waste disposal.

The *packaging* of nuclear wastes for transportation to temporary storage sites and ultimately to permanent repositories has been given very high priority for funding by the U.S. Department of Energy. Sandia Laboratories has developed waste containers that can remain sealed even if trucks carrying them are struck by high-speed locomotives and engulfed in flame.† The conditions designed for these experiments far exceeded those assumed likely, and no release of radioactive materials has been noted. Certainly the risks from transport of radioactive wastes are far less than other risks now accepted by the public for transportation. (See the discussion of chemical spills due to accidents in Chapter 8.)

Cement and calcines can be used for storage of radioactive low-level wastes. Various high-temperature and pressure glasses and supercalcines in metal cannisters and artificially grown minerals which will structurally bond radioactive elements can be used for high-level and transuranic wastes. The technology to safely isolate radioactive materials into various waste forms is also available.**The remaining questions in-

*Cowan, op. cit.
†R. N. Pope, R.F. Luna, H. R. Yoshimura, and J. D. McClure, "The Environmental Effects Associated with the Transportation of Radioactive Materials," Second International Conference on Scientific Basis for Nuclear Waste Management, Cambridge, Mass., November 1979.
**R. Roy, "Nuclear Wastes: A Solid Solution," *The Sciences* 19 (1979): 12-19.

clude economic factors, reprocessing fuel before burial, and final decisions on waste forms for different types of radioactive wastes.

Three Mile Island

While the nuclear industry has the best safety record of any energy-producing industry, it is not without risk. Certainly the most serious nuclear power plant accident occurred at Metropolitan Edison's Three Mile Island–2 Reactor on March 28, 1979. When coolant was lost to the core of the reactor and a backup system failed, there was serious damage to the core, a large amount of radioactivity released to the containment building, and some radioactivity released to the atmosphere. Although media coverage of the accident was often sensational, it is true that the public was not adequately informed. More importantly, the accident demonstrated that human error coupled with some valve and other minor instrument failures caused the coolant loss. With routine inspection on a regular basis as required by law, the accident could have been prevented. People living near the Three Mile Island–2 Reactor were not adequately informed of what had happened, what measures were being taken to correct the situation, and whether they should evacuate the area.

The total amount of radiation and radioactivity emitted to the environment was very low. Iodine-131 was found to be well below the limits set by the Environmental Protection Agency (EPA). Other radioactive species such as cesium-137 were not detected above background levels. Two million people live within 80 kilometers of the reactor; and the average individual dose in this area was 1.5 mrem,* well under the 100-mrem level set by the Nuclear Regulatory Commission (NRC) and the EPA. From a 100-mrem dose there is a 1-in-50,000 chance that a person will develop cancer—much higher than the 1-in-7 normal incidence of cancer in the population. Health effect calculations indicate one excess cancer fatality is likely in the area, compared with 325,000 fatalities normally predicted for 2 million people.[†]

Despite the fact that the amount of radiation and radioactive isotopes emitted from the reactor was low, the public was for the most part frightened. The Kemeny Commission appointed by the president investigated the incident and offered the following recommendations (in modified form here):

1. The NRC must be restructured to ensure smoother functioning.

---

*mrem = milliroentgen-equivalent-man; i.e., different individuals will react differently to absolute amounts of radioactivity.

[†]R. A. Knief, *Nuclear Energy Technology* (New York: Hemisphere Publishing Company with McGraw-Hill Book Company, in press).

2. The nuclear industry must improve its attitude toward safety and regulation of nuclear power plants.

3. Greater emphasis must be placed on operator training.

4. Person-to-machine control must be improved with more emphasis on risk assessment, instrument corrections, and backup systems.

5. More research is needed on low-level radiation and its effects.

6. Emergency planning and response by the utilities and national, state, and local governing boards must be upgraded and coupled with an all-out effort to educate the public on radioactivity and nuclear power.

7. The public has a right to "up-to-the-minute" information if an emergency occurs, and steps to prevent erroneous or misleading information must be taken.

Steps have already been taken to correct these shortcomings, but it should be emphasized that these recommended measures are for the most part only enforcing regulations in effect at the time of the accident.

Obviously there is no "bright" side to a nuclear accident. However, backup systems did work sufficiently well to prevent serious core damage.* Thus this "billion-dollar experiment" demonstrated that certain catastrophic events (e.g., core meltdown, release of excessive amounts of radiation with loss of life and permanent damage to the environment, and evacuation of hundreds of thousands of people) did not happen as some opponents of nuclear power had predicted.

The effects of the Three Mile Island–2 Reactor accident can be divided into two types: tangible and intangible. The tangible effects are those described earlier plus an ultimate cost of about $1 billion for investigation time, reactor downtime, clean-up procedures, repair, inspections, return to licensing, and lost revenue. Hence the accident is called a "billion-dollar experiment" based on the approximate expense to make the reactor operative again. The intangible effects are more difficult to assess. It is well known that many people fear radiation and that many individuals are reluctant to continue living near the Three Mile Island–2 Reactor. Decreased property values and other effects on area residents cannot adequately be put into "dollars and cents." Furthermore, the antinuclear groups in the United States are even more convinced of their stand, and this can only delay many aspects of nuclear power development. Despite this, nuclear power advocates have reinforced their points that nothing catastrophic did happen at Three Mile Island–2 and that nuclear power accidents can be prevented by the NRC, EPA, and other

*"A Preliminary Report on Three Mile Island," *Science* 203 (1979): 280-81.

groups. If other accidents occur, they will probably be similar to the one at Three Mile Island–2, where the ultimate damage is to the economy rather than to public safety or the environment.

Other Energy Sources

Hydroelectric Energy

Hydroelectric energy now plays an important role in the United States, but its role will diminish in the future. To significantly increase hydroelectric energy in the United States would require dam construction on an unparalleled scale. This is not likely to occur for several reasons. First, there is some evidence that overdamming of our rivers is neither necessary nor desirable due to the problems of proper water allocations downstream from possible dam sites. Second, some of the hypothetically favorable sites are located in wilderness areas and it is unlikely that dam construction in these areas would be approved. Third, even though it is cheaper per kilowatt-hour than other sources, hydroelectric energy cannot compete with the other forms of energy in an age of escalating construction costs and other factors. Therefore, while the amount of energy provided from hydroelectric sources will continue to increase in the next quarter-century, the rate of energy consumption will increase at a greater pace. Hence, hydroelectric energy will contribute a lower percentage to total energy production.

Geothermal Energy

Geothermal energy has received favorable attention in several parts of the world, including the United States. Several types of geothermal energy production are available. Using natural steam from hot springs such as The Geysers in California has proven successful. This field provides 15 percent of the electrical energy needed for San Francisco, which is 75 miles (120 kilometers) away. Some of the highest concentrations of radon are recorded from hot spring areas like The Geysers, as well as high doses of hydrogen sulfide and trace metals. Many of the other natural steam fields are located in isolated parts of the western United States well removed from urban centers, hence power transmission becomes a major problem. Areas with natural steam potential are shown in Figure 7–20.

Another source of geothermal energy utilizes heat of rocks by the so-called *hot-dry-rock* method being developed at the Los Alamos Scientific Laboratory since 1973. This method uses areas of above-normal

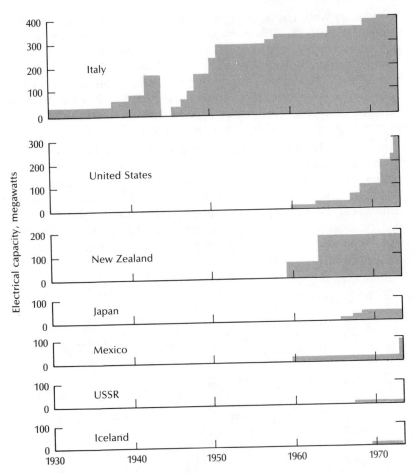

FIGURE 7–20 Use of natural steam fields. The steam fields at Larderello, Italy, and Waireiki, New Zealand, have been in use for many years; and The Geysers in Sonomo County, California, have been an important producer of electrical energy from steam for the past fifteen years. San Francisco may obtain as much as 60 percent of its electrical energy needs from The Geysers by the year 2000. Unfortunately, natural steam fields are commonly located far from urban centers and transmission costs prevent their widespread application.

heat flow within the earth. These areas are located near recent volcanism in the western United States (Figure 7–20). Several wells are drilled through Phanerozoic rocks into Precambrian basement rocks to a depth (about 3 kilometers near Los Alamos) where high heat flow produces high temperatures. Techniques developed by the petroleum industry are used to fracture the rocks. Water is then introduced at depth by an *injection well* and is heated by the rocks to produce steam. The water, connected

ENERGY

to recovery wells by the fractures, is pumped to the surface in the form of steam (Figure 7–21). This method's advantages are clean energy, an essentially infinite source of heat, a small environmental impact, and a cost competitive with other forms of electrical energy. The disadvantages are few: They include random geographic distribution of high heat flow areas, possible introduction of some trace element carcinogens to the environment, increased drilling costs, and unanswered questions about the length of time the fractures may remain open.

The hot-dry-rock program may be used to produce hot water in areas of lower natural heat flow. This hot water could be used for space heating by industry and commercial enterprises, especially where solar energy is not feasible. In areas such as the northeastern United States drilling can be carried out to depths where water will be heated to the vaporization point. This warm water could be used for many purposes, but since industry uses roughly 40 percent of its energy for space heating, this application is attractive.*

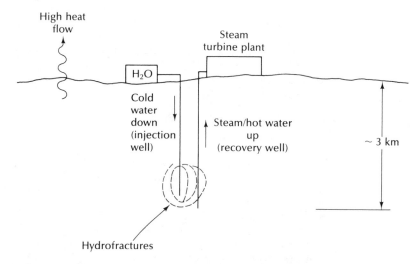

FIGURE 7–21 Hot-dry-rock geothermal method. Steam can also be produced by using areas (usually areas of volcanic activity) where the subsurface heat flow is much higher than normal. In such an area near Los Alamos, New Mexico, drilling to a depth of 3 kilometers revealed sufficient heat to convert water to steam. This method works by pumping water down an injection well to an area where the rocks have been hydrofractured. The water is heated by the natural rock environment, and steam is returned to the surface and then to a steam-powered turbine plant. The Los Alamos project first produced steam by this method in March 1977.

*For more information, refer to the ERDA Workshop on Geothermal Energy, 1975.

Solar Energy

Solar energy has been attractive since early times. The amount of heat energy from the sun is so great that comparing it with other energy sources is nearly meaningless. Technologically, we have not yet found a way to economically reap benefits from solar energy except on a very small scale in the West and Southwest. If technological breakthroughs allow solar heating to be feasible nationwide, energy relief in other areas will be felt, but not before the twenty-first century. Solar desalination of water could be made economical with combined solar-nuclear plants near saline lakes.

The Oceans as a Source of Energy

The oceans contain enough potential energy to serve the world forever. The abundant but widely distributed amounts of uranium and thorium alone could fuel nuclear reactors for millions of years. Extraction is not likely, however, since these elements are more concentrated on the continents. Rather, the use of ocean tides, thermal gradients, currents, and salinity gradients is being explored.

Tides are now being used to produce energy in pilot plants, but no real contribution to the world's energy supply is likely before the twenty-first century. Ocean currents are enormous and swift in several places on the earth, but harnessing their energy is still in the theoretical stage. Demonstration plants using the power of ocean currents are many years off even though the principle of using water force to operate turbines is the same. To take advantage of the ocean thermal gradient, which is 20°C in some places from the surface to 2000 feet (600 meters) deep, we would need a unique type of "mining." That is, an organic substance like anhydrous ammonia could be heated in a floating energy conversion plant and the energy transmitted to land. Large floating plants may be constructed for this purpose in the twenty-first century. Salinity currents result when fresh water or sea water flows into a brine, releasing vast amount of energy. The very dense saline rivers flowing into the oceans are such a resource, but they await technological advances. In addition, this form of energy is renewable through the hydrologic cycle.

Another energy resource is *biomass*, that carbon-bearing organic material present in the oceans. Plans to use biomass for distilling organic liquids—including methane, methanol, and ethanol—are being explored both for fuels and for power generation.

The oceans' major energy resource will ultimately be the hydrogen they contain, which will be used in nuclear fusion.

Nuclear Fusion

Nuclear fusion—unlike nuclear fission, which releases energy when atoms split—releases energy when two or more atoms are fused together. Since the methods now being considered involve either deuterium in water, H^2 (i.e., hydrogen with an extra neutron), or the more abundant H^1, a potentially infinite energy source is available. Methods using energy from nuclear fusion, however, will require great technological advances. Temperatures in excess of one million degrees Kelvin may be required, and the only way to contain such energy is by intense magnetic fields. Although nuclear fusion research is continuing, it is unlikely that fusion will contribute to our energy supply until well into the twenty-first century.

Geochemistry and Human Impact on the Environment

Environmental Geochemistry

For the last decade or so there has been a concentrated effort to determine if certain diseases or other health problems can be linked to soil, water, and geochemistry. The National Institute of Health and other organizations have investigated the effects of carcinogens such as insecticides and fungicides on the ecosystem by looking at virtually all forms of organic life from protozoa to people; however, little had been done until about the mid-1960s to relate rocks or soils to health problems.

In 1971 H. L. Cannon and H. C. Hopps published "Environmental Geochemistry in Health and Disease,"* which was followed by another article in 1972, "Geochemical Environment in Relation to Health and Disease"†—both welcome additions to geosciences literature. The latter article was the result of papers presented before representatives of the medical profession as well as geoscientists. Unfortunately, there were too few representatives of the medical profession present for a meaningful exchange of ideas. This is part of the problem. Scientists, led by those from the State of Missouri and the U.S. Geological Survey, have compiled an impressive amount of data over the last fifteen years. Each year a conference on trace substances and environmental health is

---

*H. L. Cannon and H. C. Hopps, "Environmental Geochemistry in Health and Disease," Geological Society of American Memoir 123, 1971.

†H. L. Cannon and H. C. Hopps, "Geochemical Environment in Relation to Health and Disease," N. Y. Academy of Science *Annals*, 199 (1972): 388.

held in Rolla, Missouri, sponsored by the Geochemical Society, the State of Missouri, and others. Attendance is generally poor, the data are not distributed as rapidly nor as widely as is desirable, and the average person is usually unaware of the information presented. This is unfortunate because carefully documented data are reported at these meetings and in subsequent publications.

For example, it has long been apparent in the vicinity of sulfide-ore mines that, prior to regulation, large amounts of potentially carcinogenic materials were being indiscriminantly dumped into streams and ponds, or allowed to escape into the atmosphere. The effects of some carcinogens (e.g., mercury and cadmium) in promoting disease and other health problems have been known for a long time, and measures have been taken to remedy obvious hazards. Not so obvious are the effects of trace substances released into the environment by industrial progress, including ventures concerned with earth resources *and* other activities not associated with mining. Highway construction often causes more land to be excavated than would many mining efforts. Some trace substances are so locked up in rocks that normal weathering does not allow them to be released rapidly. If the delicate balance between soil or rock and rain is disturbed, however, once immobile elements can be dissolved, transported, and concentrated.

Concentration of a potentially carcinogenic substance is very complex. The process includes water concentration, uptake by plants, further concentration by ingestion of the plants by animals (e.g., cattle), and even further concentration in people (e.g., when they eat hamburgers). More potential carcinogens may be added if the hamburgers are grilled over charcoal, because organic matter is an excellent chelating and complexing agent for many carcinogenic metals like those concentrated in coals. Thus, from soil disturbed by excavation to human ingestion there may be as much as a hundredfold increase in the concentration of certain potentially carcinogenic substances. While you may consider this example somewhat extreme, it is not as precise as we would like. There are too few quantitative data to properly assess spots in the food chain where excessive concentration of carcinogens may take place. It is not sufficient to monitor only one spot. All steps in the process—from the original soil or rock, through the transporting media (including airborne materials), and concentration in plants—must be very carefully monitored.

Occasionally the uptake of trace metals (e.g., selenium, uranium, or titanium) by plants can be used to indicate above-normal levels of one or more elements in the soil. Such plants are known as *accumulator plants*. At times they may be used as biogeochemical indicators in searching for ore deposits. A few plants known to concentrate specific elements are

> *Astragalus* (locoweed)—selenium (its occurrence is common in areas over seleniferous coals and commonly over sedimentary uranium deposits)
>
> *Clethra* (alder)—cobalt
>
> *Nyssa* (gum tree)—cobalt
>
> *Ilex glabra* (holly)—zinc
>
> *Carya* (hickory)—beryllium, rare earth elements, barium,and scandium

Uptake usually depends on the availability of the elements in the soil.

We distinguish between trace elements added to the environment from weathering of rocks and trace elements added by fertilizer compounds (all fertilizing agents, insecticides, and fungicides). Some elements enriched in soil due to chemicals and natural wastes used in agriculture include chromium, iodine, lithium, lead, zinc, cadmium, and copper. Because uptake data are commonly erratic, virtually every combined agricultural chemical in any one specific land area should, if possible, be analyzed to see if trace elements are being added to the food system in amounts above or below the recommended dose. Remember also that anomalously-low as well as anomalously-high levels of certain elements can be toxic to plants and animals (Table 8–1). Some major elements such as iron and silicon have been omitted from Table 8–1; high amounts of either may be carcinogenic. Also omitted are elements such as barium and platinum, which, if improperly monitored during milling and purifying, may be carcinogenic.

We will discuss radioactive species later in this chapter when we compare coal- and nuclear-fired power plants. In general, background levels of naturally occurring radioactive species are not well established. At times, an inverse correlation exists between land over uranium deposits with near-normal radon emission and widely disseminated uranium in areas over which above-normal radon emission is measured. Radioactivity in water is also difficult to assess. High radioactivity of mine water is expected and monitored, yet water far removed from uranium mining is commonly more radioactive than expected. Reasons for this erratic behavior are not well understood.

Mercury deserves some special mention here. It is a scarce element yet is easy to recover from ore by simple roasting (see Chapter 4). This characteristic—its volatility—makes it very difficult to control, however. If mercury is locked tightly into its main ore mineral, cinnabar (HgS), it is relatively inert if ingested by animals and may not harm them at all. If mercury is converted to an organic form, either as monomethyl or dimethyl mercury, it is not only hazardous but extremely easy to concentrate in animal organs. We have already described mercury poisoning

TABLE 8–1   Effects of high or low concentrations of trace elements on plants and animals.

Element	Effects
Lithium	Low levels may cause mania in humans.
Fluorine	Low levels cause low growth rates in rats and dental decay in humans. High levels may affect plants and cause bone abnormalities in humans.
Chromium	Toxic in high amounts to some plants; also toxic as Cr^{6+} in animals in some regions.
Nickel	High amounts are not commonly toxic; as inhaled metallic dust and as nickel carbonyl, however, is toxic in humans.
Copper	Low copper content causes impaired growth in some plants and anemia in humans. High amounts are toxic to plants and dangerous to humans (Wilson's disease and possibly increased rate of aging).
Zinc	Low amounts cause stunted growth in plants and all animals, plus other deleterious effects. High amounts are toxic in plants.
Arsenic	Low amounts may cause hair abnormalities in some plants and animals. High amounts are toxic in all animals.
Selenium	Low amounts have been linked to many abnormalities in some plants and animals. High amounts may suppress growth in plants and cattle.
Molybdenum	Low amounts may cause growth retardation in some plants and animals. High amounts can cause a variety of diseases in cattle.
Cadmium	High amounts are thought to be toxic to plants as well as causing hypertension, sterility, and testicular hemorrhage in animals.
Iodine	Low amounts are linked to goiter in animals. High amounts are toxic to plants and humans and impair reproduction in plants and animals.
Lead	Toxic to plants and animals in high amounts. In humans, it affects the central nervous system and causes anemia, urinary disease, and bone damage.
Beryllium	Toxic in high amounts to plants and animals; humans may be more affected by industrially-produced beryllium than from natural sources.
Magnesium	Although *not* a trace element, magnesium deficiency in plants and animals seems to be linked to other diseases and may enhance them.

TABLE 8-1 (continued)

Element	Effects
Manganese	High amounts of manganese, especially when linked with other elements, may cause toxicity in infants, metabolism problems, and intestinal problems.
Tin	High amounts may cause growth abnormalities in laboratory plants and animals; its exact role is not well understood.
Vanadium	Low amounts affect the metabolism of plants and animals; high amounts from industrial exposure are occasionally toxic. No such toxicity is suspected from the normal environment.
Mercury	Toxic in high amounts to plants and animals; most high levels of mercury are directly related to industrial use. (Note: In the late nineteenth and early twentieth centuries mercury contamination from mining was widespread.)

SOURCE: H. L. Cannon and H. C. Hopps, "Geochemistry and the Environment," in *The Relation of Suspected Trace Elements to Health and Disease*, Vol. 1 (Washington, D.C.: National Academy of Sciences, 1974).

by mining and milling within the last 100 years, but mercury poisoning from industrial misuse is not well known. From 1950 to 1965 at Minamata Bay, Japan, a chemical plant discharge was responsible for 43 deaths out of 116 cases of mercury poisoning. A brief flurry of interest and concern was noted in the press at that time, but most people questioned today would have little or no knowledge of the Minamata incident.

In the period from February 1972 to August 1972 there were 6530 cases—resulting in 460 deaths— of methyl mercury poisoning in Iraq.* This was a disaster beyond description, yet even now few in the United States outside of those working in geology or environmental health are aware of it. Wheat seed that had been treated with methyl mercury fungicide was planted, and bread made with the wheat was enriched in methyl mercury. Not only was bread intake involved in the epidemic, but mercury was also concentrated by several other means: livestock were fed the contaminated wheat seed and mercury was concentrated in the meat; mercury was found in vegetation other than wheat in the wheatfield; game birds and fish fed on the contaminated seed; and some mercury was inhaled and came in contact with skin. All the fatalities occurred in districts outside metropolitan areas. What was even more unfortunate was that warnings were on the sacks of seed—but in those

*F. Bakir et al., "Methyl Mercury Poisoning in Iraq," *Science* 181 (1973): p. 230.

154

rural areas of Iraq most farmers were not even literate in their native language. This is a good example of poor governmental policies on the monitoring of such materials. The point is well made, however, that environmental contamination is caused more often by industrial-related (indirect in this case) or distribution factors than by earth resources industries where monitoring is carried out in a systematic and thorough fashion.

Land Use for Mining and Nonmining Activities

It is interesting to compare the impact of mining with nonmining activities on land availability. Urban growth in the United States is continuing to boom—this comes as no surprise; but how much land is involved? We tend to make a great deal of noise about mining ventures but say relatively little about normal urban growth and highway construction. A comparison is useful, especially since land usage plans for mining, for mining-related purposes (e.g., tailings and other waste disposal, including radioactive wastes), and for dam construction are by law accompanied by environmental impact statements. Equivalent statements for urban growth or highway construction are routinely not requested.

In the United States, approximately 700 square kilometers of land are stripped by urban construction each year. If we assume that an average of 4500 metric tons of sediment are produced per square kilometer, then some 3,100,000 metric tons of sediment are produced each year—more than three times the load of sediment carried by the Potomac River.*

Furthermore, for every kilometer of two-lane highway built, about 35 acres of land are cleared. Thus, if more than 800,000 kilometers of highway are built per ten-year period, some 43,000 square kilometers of land are available for erosion and approximately 193,500,000 metric tons of sediment may result. While precise effects of this sediment load are unknown, we do know that urban and highway construction have affected reservoir loads, natural fisheries, and marsh filling. What is not recorded are the types of sediments released. For example, what is the long-range effect of building hundreds of kilometers of highway through rocks relatively rich in carcinogenic elements? Certainly sediments provide a better chance for some elements—especially if they are soluble or easily oxidized—to be removed and possibly concentrated by erosion and

---

*Data from the U.S. government (public information pamphlets) and the National Research Council–National Academy of Sciences.

transport. The law requires monitoring during mining operations of elements identified by the scientific community as carcinogenic in humans (nickel, arsenic, and chromium) and animals (beryllium, cadmium, chromium, cobalt, iron, lead, nickel, selenium, zinc, and titanium); other metals associated with different types of disease in both humans and plants and animals (mercury compounds, copper, and vanadium); and radioactive species. No such law exists for urban construction or highway construction.

In mining areas there is a strong potential for release of carcinogenic or potentially carcinogenic elements above threshold level values (TLVs) proposed by the National Institute of Occupational Safety and Health (NIOSH), the Occupational Safety and Health Administration (OSHA), and the Mining Enforcement and Safety Administration (MESA). The TLV refers to the highest level of a substance that a person can be exposed to without suffering harmful effects.* But TLVs are poorly defined and even more poorly understood in that knowing the abundance of a potential carcinogen alone is insufficient to establish health effects. Elements are monitored in areas of active mining, but not necessarily in other types of excavations.

Let us now compare land use for all mining with that for specific mining ventures. The National Research Council–National Academy of Sciences has estimated that the total mining, milling, and processing of minerals in the United States results in some 1500 metric tons of materials per year, compared with 3 million metric tons per year from urban construction and more than 19 million metric tons per year from highway construction. Remember also that many of the sediments from mining ventures are used as backfill, stored, or in other ways somewhat isolated from the ecosystem. (This applies to some, but certainly not all, mining ventures.) Similarly, some of the 22 million metric tons of sediment created by urban and highway construction is used for fill and thus is not subjected to severe erosion. Still we can realistically ask how the effects of monitored mining ventures compare with unmonitored construction for nonmining purposes in the same area (e.g., an area rich in selenium at or near the surface). To properly evaluate this we need to know the area's geochemistry before *any* mining or nonmining venture is undertaken; and generally this is unknown. The vigorous testing of the United States (48 contiguous states plus Alaska) by the early 1980s with one sample per 10 square kilometers should provide invaluable data for uranium and thorium; but only in some areas were multielement analyses proposed. Why the Department of Health, Education, and Welfare did not help defray the cost of this survey by the Department of Energy is also unknown.

---

*New York Academy of Science, "Cancer and the Worker", 1977, p. 180.

GEOCHEMISTRY AND HUMAN IMPACT ON THE ENVIRONMENT

Coal-based Versus
Nuclear-based Technology

The merits of coal-based and nuclear-based electrical energy technologies have been hotly debated. The argument used by the advocates of a coal-based technology combines the availability of coal with claims for clean burning by the time it is used on a large scale. It is coupled with the idea that "you're safer with coal than with radioactivity." Those who advocate nuclear-based technology counter with arguments that coal is potentially more harmful to the environment than nuclear fuel in terms of mining, coal is less efficient, coal reserves and resources are not limitless while uranium reserves and resources are abundant, and radioactive wastes can be safely handled.

Compare these two alternatives for plants generating 1000 megawatts of electricity.* For the coal-fired plant, some 200 acres of land will be affected by mining and another 300 to 400 acres for the plant site. These figures compare with 13 acres for the mining associated with a conventional light-water reactor; but keep in mind that this acreage is needed primarily for coal mining for use in the gaseous diffusion plants—not just for uranium ore! Finally, only 0.05 acre must be mined for a 1000-megawatt breeder reactor. Plant sites for nuclear facilities vary from 50 to 150 acres. Clearly, more land is involved with coal-based technology. A vital question is, Can we afford to indiscriminately mine low-grade coal without addressing all environmental issues?

Let us now compare both types of technologies in terms of effluents, wastes, and thermal effects. Burning coal releases large amounts of many substances into the atmosphere. For the 1000-megawatt plant some 45,000 tons (40,835 metric tons) of sulfur dioxide; 26,000 tons (23,590 metric tons) of various nitrogen oxides; 750 tons (680 metric tons) of carbon monoxide; 3500 tons (3175 metric tons) of various particulates; and 260 tons (235 metric tons) of cyanide are released per year. For nuclear-based industries these same substances result from the coal used, but only in the amounts of 1500 tons (1360 metric tons) of sulfur dioxide, 900 tons (815 metric tons) of nitrogen oxides, 25 tons (23 metric tons) of carbon monoxide, 120 tons (110 metric tons) of other particulates, and 9 tons (8 metric tons) of cyanide. For a breeder reactor, since coal-fired plants are not part of the plan, there are no releases into the atmosphere of any of these materials. Radioactivity is released from burning coal as well as from nuclear power plants, but figures are only known for the latter. For nuclear power plants, a range from 2000 to 250,000 curies per year has been estimated by the Nuclear Regulatory Commission. The

*W. A. Fowler, *Energy and the Environment* (New York: McGraw-Hill, 1975), p. 246.

amount of radioactivity released from burning coal may actually be larger than the 250,000 curies per year from nuclear power plants, but data are too sketchy to resolve this question. The U.S. government has, however, provided data on the effects of radiation on life expectancy, as shown in Table 8–2. While semiquantitative at best, these data indicate that amounts of radiation from nuclear energy and from coal are comparable.

TABLE 8–2 Decreased life expectancy from human-caused radiation.

Medical	Natural Gas	Air Travel	Television	Nuclear Energy	Coal
4 days	3 hours	1.5 hours	8 minutes	2 minutes	2 minutes

SOURCE: U.S. Nuclear Regulatory Commission.

How coal-fired power plants affect the release of radioactive materials to the atmosphere is of critical importance. As much as 40 percent of the radium-226 detected in the atmosphere over the United States may be due to burning coal in power plants.* For example, near the coal-burning power plants in the Four Corners Region of New Mexico the radium-226 concentrations at distances of 9.3 kilometers upwind, 5.6 kilometers downwind, and 18.5 kilometers downwind were 18, 34, and 70 dpm (disintegrations per minute) per 10^5 cubic meters. This is much higher than the mean of 4.4 ± 2.5 dpm/10^5 m^3 for normal background based on samples taken in Kansas and Colorado from sites well removed from power plants both in space and wind direction. The difference in these figures is partly because the equipment used to remove airborne particulates containing carcinogenic materials like radium-226 is only about 75 percent efficient. While particulate removal by *scrubbers* can undoubtedly be improved, the use of many more coal plants will offset such improvements. When tremendous amounts of other carcinogens added to the ecosystem from burning coal are considered, then this energy source is, from a health viewpoint, less desirable than the nuclear alternative.

When we consider nonradioactive wastes, a 1000-megawatt coal plant produces 200,000 cubic feet (5660 cubic meters) of ashes and 300,000 cubic feet (8500 cubic meters) of limestone per year. The figures for the amount of coal used in the nuclear plants are 7000 and 10,000 tons respectively. There are no such wastes for breeder reactors, although they do produce plutonium. The ashes and limestone require further comment. Flue ash, in particular, is enriched in elements such as selenium,

*H. E. Moore and S. E. Poet, "Background Levels of ^{226}Ra in the Lower Troposphere," *Atmospheric Environment* 10(1978): 381-83.

GEOCHEMISTRY AND HUMAN IMPACT ON THE ENVIRONMENT

beryllium, arsenic, molybdenum, zinc, cadmium, mercury, lead, chromium, *and* radioactive uranium, thorium, and radium. While some ash is used as fill and is monitored, no accurate data are available as to how the environment is enriched in these and other elements—in highly transportable form—from the ash. The limestone, too, can be enriched in some elements considered carcinogenic, including strontium, lead, zinc, and manganese, which are also more readily available to enter the ecosystem.

Radioactive wastes are difficult to assess for coal-fired plants. We know that coals are enriched in uranium and other radioactive heavy elements.* The uranium in various coals is not removed during mining, processing, or power plant operation; hence wastes are difficult if not impossible to assess. The ash is laden with relatively mobile uranium and with highly mobile radium as well. Light-water and breeder reactors are thought to produce in the range of 8000 to 12,000 cubic feet (225 to 335 cubic meters) of ash per year, amounts which can be not only monitored but condensed into transportable forms with existing technology. Only light-water reactor waste is now being generated; breeder reactors are not yet on-line. (See Chapter 7 for a discussion of waste storage.)

Uranium mining is carefully controlled. Mine workers are monitored for radiation and wear proper clothing. Ventilation systems to remove radon gas and particulates are the best in the country. When the uranium is concentrated during milling, the tailings are cleaned of their radium by treatment with barium salts so that the radium is virtually 100 percent removed as an insoluble sulfate. Selenium, too, is confined to the tailings piles, as is arsenic. Molybdenum and vanadium are removed during the milling process, stored, and sold. Because of public concern and federal regulations, uranium mines are among the most carefully monitored mines in the United States. However, this is not true of coal mines. Hazards include black lung, explosions, fires, and cave-ins. The number of deaths and health problems due to coal processing (including burning) presumably make it many times more dangerous than equivalent (in terms of power) nuclear operations.

Only in the area of thermal pollution in water is coal power potentially less damaging than nuclear power. A 1000-megawatt coal-fired plant yields 1.1 million BTUs to water for dissipation compared with 1.8 million BTUs for nuclear plants. (The breeder reactor would yield 1.2 million BTUs.) This heat release to water is usually localized and, if not, can be handled by building water-cooling tanks. Such tanks are used in Oregon and in other areas where heating local waters is dangerous to aquatic life. In areas where effects on aquatic species are not considered, the 1.8 million BTUs are dissipated within a mile or so of the plant. There

---

*It has been estimated by U.S. Department of Energy that the Chattanooga shale alone contains some 6 trillion tons of U_3O_8—many orders of magnitude more than anticipated uranium use for centuries—*but* it is largely in unminable form.

are no demands, nor plans, for handling heat released to the natural waters near coal-fired plant sites. In terms of heat effects in the air, coal plants yield about 0.4 million BTUs compared with 0.15 million BTUs for nuclear plants.

A recent study has convincingly demonstrated that radiological effects of airborne particulates from coal-fired power plants are greater than those from nuclear-fired power plants of equal generating capacity.[*] The data in this study are *minimum* values for releases of radioactive radium, C^{14}, and H^3 because they are based only on the one percent fly ash released into the atmosphere as allowed by federal regulations; but up to 8 percent fly ash has been actually released during the 1970s. The study's conclusion, however, was that the effects of these radioactive materials are less dangerous than the effects of sulfur, nitrogen oxides, and trace elements. In another study, ozone buildups are directly related to nitrogen oxide emanations from coal-fired power plants.[†] Finally, several studies of *acid rain* and its deleterious effect on the environment reported in 1979 were related to burning coal. Such burning produces atmospheric carbon dioxide, which reacts with water vapor to form carbonic acid. The carbonic acid is then removed by rainfall and is called acid rain.

Other factors of concern include short-range economic factors and long-range climatic factors. When the energy "crisis" of 1973 hit the United States, coal was thought to be the immediate answer. The coal industry, understandably, was not ready for such a responsibility. Coal exploration and development during the 1960s had slowed because nuclear power was expected to offset decreasing availability of petroleum products. Thus miners, mines, equipment, and planning were in short supply. No industry can be expected almost overnight to make up for ten to thirteen lost years, and coal is no exception. Even with drastically reduced emission controls, coal's increased contribution to our energy supply was not felt until 1978. The economics of this situation are simple. It requires more coal, more machinery, more scrubbers and air cleanup apparatus, and more environmental controls for a coal-fired technology than for a nuclear-fired technology. Radioactive waste must also be considered. First, the projected waste from commercial nuclear operations is one-fifth to one-quarter that produced from weapons and other defense work. Hence, we will have a waste problem with or without a viable nuclear industry. This waste can be handled with existing technology (expensive but safe) or contemplated technology (less expensive and safer). But what about radioactive waste from coal- or oil-burning plants? There are currently no plans for disposing this material.

[*]J. P. McBride, R. E. Moore, J. P. Witherspoon, and R. E. Blanco, "Radiological Impact of Airborne Effluents of Coal and Nuclear Plants," *Science* 202 (1978): 1045–50.

[†]D. F. Miller, A. J. Alkezweeny, J. M. Hales, and R. N. Lee, "Ozone Formation Related to Power Plant Emissions," *Science* 202 (1978): 1186-88.

160

Now let us consider the so-called *greenhouse effect*, in which continued releases of carbon monoxide and carbon dioxide into the atmosphere accumulate to the point where energy (including light) from the sun is less available to the earth's surface. The increased cloud cover coupled with this retention of earth-generated heat (natural and artificial) heats the surface and will probably result in loss of aquatic life, melting of freshwater ice, and drastic weather changes if left unchecked. While formerly disputed by many in the scientific community, the greenhouse effect is now considered to be real and may probably be with us if we rely on a coal-based technology for the generation of electric energy.

In this section we have compared the coal and nuclear industries. The data support the argument that a nuclear-based industry is cleaner, cheaper, and safer than a coal-based technology. While it is true that reactor safeguards and transportation aspects are not considered here, others have concluded that these potential hazards are slight.*

Why then has the public been reluctant to accept nuclear power? There are a number of reasons: We have lived with a coal-based technology for hundreds of years; we are unaware (for the most part) of the dangers of coal; we think of atomic bombs when reactors or radiation are mentioned; and the dangers from nuclear power have been emphasized more often than those for coal. We know now that a fulltime worker in the Carlsbad Caverns is exposed to more radon per year than a monitored uranium mine worker;† and the calculated dose for the Carlsbad worker is above the recommended TLV, whereas that for the uranium mine worker is not.

Let us now briefly compare the potential hazards of nuclear waste with hazards from other sources.** In terms of total production, the number of lethal doses *possible* per year in the United States are given in Table 8–3. The data in Table 8–3 show potential lethal dose amounts, not actual lethal doses. Tremendous amounts of lethal materials are produced and transported throughout the United States, but satisfactory shipping and handling guidelines are available and enforced only for radioactive materials. Remember the deaths due to chlorine gas alone (late 1977 to early 1978) from train derailments to see that this is true.

From 1978 to 1979 over 600,000 people had to be evacuated because train derailments caused loads of chlorine gas, phosgene, and other toxic chemicals to be released to the environment. Some people died as a result of inhaling the chemicals, but the exact figure is unknown because not all data have been assessed by the U.S. Bureau of Statistics.

---

*See E. E. Angino, "High-level and Long-lived Radioactive Waste Disposal," *Science* 198 (1977): 885–90; and B. L. Cohen, "High-level Radioactive Waste from Light Water Reactors," *Review of Modern Physics* 49 (1977): 1–19.
†M. H. Wilkening and D. E. Watkins, "Air Exchange and Radon Concentration in the Carlsbad Caverns," *Journal of Health Physics* 31 (1976): 139-42.
**Many of these data have been from sources cited in Cohen, op. cit.

The long-range effects of inhalation of chlorine gas and other chemicals are not well known.

Another interesting compilation of data involved 10-year-old nuclear waste buried to a depth of some 600 meters.* Potential cancers due to *all* radioactive materials are about an order of magnitude less than that from aluminum and several orders of magnitude less than that from normal crustal abundances of nickel, chromium, barium, and arsenic. This does not include the many biological carcinogenic agents that are potentially present. Thus natural radiation in the environment may be a greater hazard (i.e., the sources of risk are unknown) than monitored waste repositories.

TABLE 8–3 Potential lethal doses per year in the United States (based on production and consumption figures).

	Lethal Doses per Year
Inhalation	
Chlorine	4×10^{14}
Phosgene	2×10^{13}
Ammonia	6×10^{12}
Hydrogen cyanide	6×10^{12}
Nuclear waste*	1.6×10^{11}
Ingestion	
Barium	9×10^{10}
Arsenic	1×10^{10}
Nuclear waste*	8×10^{10}

*Nuclear waste assumed to be 10 years old following present U.S. government policy.

Chemical Wastes

Unlike mining, milling, and earth excavations due to road construction and other nonmining activities, where the materials moved about are monitored, chemical wastes are usually dumped indiscriminately about the country. There may be more than 100,000 illegal chemical dumping sites in the United States; and this includes only fairly large sites. Smaller, illegal dumping takes place almost everywhere.

The hazards posed by the illegal dumping of chemical wastes are only recently receiving the attention they deserve. The Love Canal

*Cohen, op. cit.

incidents present a good example of these hazards. David Rall, Director of the National Institute for Environmental Health Sciences, has stated

> The important scientific problems at Love Canal are that little is known about the toxicity of the chemicals, and that it is difficult to use health surveys and epidemiological studies to associate exposure to chemicals from dump sites with human health effects. We do not have markers that help us associate disease with prior chemical exposures. Moreover, in a statistical sense, most dump areas impact on the health of relatively few people, and it is difficult to detect rare events in small populations. Because we can't generalize about the toxic effects of multiple chemical exposure, it is almost impossible to estimate the health impacts of such exposure other than to assume that they are simply additive.

This is a sad commentary. New York State and the Environmental Protection Agency have identified some 80 chemicals at Love Canal, 11 of which are suspected human carcinogens and one, benzene, a known carcinogen to humans. Claims for some $11 billion in damages have been filed against the Hooker Chemical Company, the firm which first used the canal for approved dumping of chemical wastes. As more and more data are gathered, the picture becomes increasingly more complex, creating trauma among the people still living near the canal.

There are several key items which should have, and could have, been stressed before dumping was allowed. The geology and hydrology of the original site were not properly investigated, nor was follow-up monitoring of the canal carried out by federal, state, or company groups (although it is certainly not clear who is liable here). Background inorganic and organic geochemical testing of the soils, water, and rock of the site and surrounding area prior to dumping was unknown.

While the Love Canal incident is now well publicized, consider the illegal dumping sites throughout the country. There is little data and few identified approaches to dealing with such illegal dumping. Unlike the Nuclear Regulatory Commission, which keeps a rigid control on the nuclear industry, the Federal Regulatory Commission does not have sufficient clout nor personnel to monitor the disposal of nonradioactive chemical wastes. Remember that most of these materials, although carcinogenic, are not radioactive and thus will not decay away with time; once dumped they are a permanent part of the environment.

When the geochemistry of the natural environment is adequately known sometime in the future, then we can be guaranteed that (1) sites safe for low-level radioactive and hazardous chemical waste dumping can be safely identified, and (2) rocks, soils, and waters naturally high in carcinogenic elements will be identified. Furthermore, from these data it should be possible to detect where many of the illegal dump sites are located, and monitoring or cleanup will be initiated. Steps toward these ends must be taken; in fact, they are long overdue. Future generations should be able to believe that hazardous waste sites were cleaned up where possible, that sites where cleanup was impossible or limited are being monitored, and that sites selected for all types of waste disposal will not pose a threat to them.

Additional Readings

Chapter 1

Brobst, D. A., and Pratt, W. P., eds. 1973. *United States mineral resources.* U.S. Geological Survey Professional Paper 820.

Cameron, E. N., ed., 1973. *The mineral position of the United States, 1975–2000.* Madison: University of Wisconsin Press.

Committee on Geological Sciences, National Research Council. 1972. *The earth and human affairs.* San Francisco: Canfield Press.

Committee on Resources and Man, National Research Council. 1969. *Resources and man.* San Francisco: W. H. Freeman.

Flawn, P. T. 1966. *Environmental geology.* New York: Harper and Row.

Kesler, S. E. 1976. *Our finite mineral resources.* New York: McGraw-Hill.

Landsberg, H. H. 1964. *Natural resources for U.S. growth: A look ahead to the year 2000.* Baltimore: Johns Hopkins University Press.

Laporte, L. F. 1975. *Encounter with the earth: Materials and processes.* San Francisco: Canfield Press.

Laporte, L. F. 1975. *Encounter with the earth: Resources.* San Francisco: Canfield Press.

Lovering, T. S. 1943. *Minerals in world affairs.* Englewood Cliffs, N. J.: Prentice-Hall.

McDivitt, J. F., and Manners, G. 1974. *Minerals and men.* Baltimore: Johns Hopkins University Press.

National Academy of Sciences. 1975. *Mineral resources and the environment.* A report prepared by the Committee on Mineral Resources and the Environment.

Skinner, B. J. 1976. *Earth resources.* Englewood Cliffs, N. J.: Prentice-Hall.

Skinner, B. J., and Turekian, K. K. 1973. *Man and the ocean.* Englewood Cliffs, N. J.: Prentice-Hall.

U.S. Bureau of Mines. 1976. *Mineral facts and problems.* U.S. Bureau of Mines Bulletin 630.

_____. (Published annually.) *Minerals yearbook: Metals, minerals and fuels.* Vols. I and II.

Chapter 2

Bateman, A. M. 1950. *Economic mineral deposits.* 2d ed. New York: John Wiley & Sons.

Buddington, A. F. 1933. Correlation of kinds of igneous rocks with kinds of mineralization. In *Ore deposits of the western states,* ed. W. Lindgren, pp. 350–85. New York: American Institute of Mining and Metallurgical Engineers.

Lamey, C. A. 1966. *Metallic and industrial mineral deposits*. New York: McGraw-Hill.

Lindgren, W. 1933. *Mineral deposits*. 4th ed. New York: McGraw-Hill.

Noble, J. A. 1955. The classification of ore deposits. *Economic Geology* (special issue): 155–69.

Park, C. F., and MacDiarmid, R. A. 1970. *Ore deposits*. 2d ed. San Francisco: W. H. Freeman.

Ridge, J. D., ed. 1968. *Ore deposits of the United States 1933–67*. Vols. I and II. New York: American Institute of Mining, Metallurgical and Petroleum Engineers.

Stanton, R. L. 1972. *Ore petrology*. New York: McGraw-Hill.

Thomas, L. J. 1973. *An introduction to mining*. Sydney, Australia: Hicks Smith and Sons.

Chapter 3

Davis, S. N., and Dewiest, R. J. M. 1966. *Hydrogeology*. New York: John Wiley & Sons.

Dewiest, R. J. M. 1965. *Geohydrology*. New York: John Wiley & Sons.

Fox, C. S. 1949. *The geology of water supply*. London: London's Technical Press.

Gross, M. G. 1980. *Oceanography*. 4th ed. Columbus, Ohio: Charles E. Merrill.

McGuinness, C. L. 1963. *The role of ground water in the national water situation*. U.S. Geological Survey Water Supply Paper No. 1800.

Turekian, K. K. 1968. *Oceans*. Englewood Cliffs, N. J.: Prentice-Hall.

United Nations Publication. 1976. *Water desalination in developing countries*.

U.S. Department of Agriculture. 1955. Water. In *The yearbook of agriculture*.

Walton, W. C. 1970. *Groundwater resource evaluation*. New York: McGraw-Hill.

Wolman, A. 1962. Water Resources Publication 1000-B. Washington, D. C.: Research Council–National Academy of Sciences.

_____. 1965. Metabolism of cities. *Scientific American* 213:30.

Chapter 4

Amstutz, G. C., and Bernard, A. J. 1973. *Ores in sediments*. International Union of Geological Sciences, Series A, No. 3. Berlin: Springer-Verlag.

Bateman, A. M. 1950. *Economic mineral deposits*. 2d ed. New York: John Wiley & Sons.

_____. 1951. *The formation of mineral deposits*. New York: John Wiley & Sons.

ADDITIONAL READINGS

Buddington, A. F. 1933. Correlation of kinds of igneous rocks with kinds of mineralization. In *Ore deposits of the western states* (Lindgren Volume), pp. 350–85. New York: American Institute of Mining and Metallurgical Engineers.

Douglas, R. J. W., ed. 1970. *Geology and economic minerals of Canada.* Economic Geology Report No. 1, Geological Survey of Canada.

Lindgren, W. 1933. *Mineral deposits.* 4th ed. New York: McGraw-Hill.

Noble, J. A. 1955. The classification of ore deposits. *Economic geology* (special issue): 155–69.

Park, C. F., Jr., and MacDiarmid, R. A. 1970. *Ore deposits.* 2d ed. San Francisco: W. H. Freeman.

Ridge, J. D., ed. 1968. *Ore deposits of the United States, 1933/67.* Vols. I and II. New York: American Institute of Mining, Metallurgical and Petroleum Engineers.

Routhier, P. 1963. *Les gisements metalliferes.* Tomes I et II. Paris: Masson.

Stanton, R. L. 1972. *Ore petrology.* New York: McGraw-Hill.

Titley, S. R., and Hicks, C. L. 1966. *Geology of the porphyry copper deposits of southwestern North America.* Tucson: University of Arizona Press.

Warren, K. 1973. *Mineral resources.* New York: John Wiley & Sons.

Chapter 5

Bates, R. L. 1960. *Geology of the industrial rocks and minerals.* New York: Harper & Row.

Borchert, H., and Muir, R. O. 1964. *Salt deposits—The origin, metamorphism, and deformation of evaporites.* Princeton, N. J.: Van Nostrand.

Gillson, J. L. et al. 1960. *Industrial minerals and rocks.* Seeley W. Mudd Series, 3rd ed. New York: American Institute of Mining, Metallurgical and Petroleum Engineers.

Lamey, C. A. 1966. *Metallic and industrial mineral deposits.* New York: McGraw-Hill.

Skinner, B. J. et al., eds. 1979. An issue devoted to phosphate, potash, and sulfur. *Economic Geology,* vol. 74.

Chapter 6

Flawn, P. T. 1970. *Environmental geology.* New York: Harper and Row.

Griggs, G. B., and Gilchrist, J. A. 1977. *The earth and land use planning.* North Scituate, Mass.: Duxbury Press.

Legget, R. F. 1973. *Cities and geology.* New York: McGraw-Hill.

ADDITIONAL READINGS

Chapter 7

Dansereau, P., ed. 1970. *Challenge for survival: Land, air and water for man in megalopolis*. New York: Columbia University Press.

Fisher, J.C. 1974. *Energy crises in perspective*. New York: John Wiley & Sons.

Fowler, J.M. 1975. *Energy and the environment*. New York: McGraw-Hill.

Halacy, D.S., Jr. 1977. *Earth, water, wind and sun*: *Our energy alternatives*. New York: Harper and Row.

Hammond, A.L.; Metz, W.D.; and Maugh, T.H. 1973. *Energy and the future*. Washington, D.C.: American Association for the Advancement of Science.

Odum, H.T., and Odum, E.C. 1976. *Energy basis for man and nature*. New York: McGraw-Hill.

Reynolds, W.C. 1974. *Energy*: *From nature to man*. New York: McGraw-Hill.

Young, L.B. 1973. *Power over people*. London: Oxford Press.

Chapter 8

Duce, R.A., ed. 1974. *Pollutant transfer to the marine environment*. NSF/IDOE Pollutant Transfer Workshop.

Enthoven, A.C., and Freeman, A.M., eds. 1973. *Pollution, resources, and the environment*. New York: W.W. Norton.

Fagan, J.J. 1974. *The earth environment*. Englewood Cliffs, N.J.: Prentice-Hall.

Hines, L.G. 1973. *Environmental issues: Population, pollution, and economics*. New York: W.W. Norton.

Schneider, M.J. 1979. *Persistent poisons: Chemical pollutants in the environment*. New York: New York Academy of Sciences.

Singer, S.F., ed. 1970. *Global effects of environmental pollution*. Symposium of the American Association for the Advancement of Science, December 1968. New York: Springer-Verlag.

Tank, R.W., ed. 1973. *Focus on environmental geology*. New York: Oxford Press.

Turk, A.; Turk, J.; and Wittes, J.T. 1972. *Ecology pollution environment*. Philadelphia: W.B. Saunders.

Appendices

APPENDIX 1 The average composition of continental crustal rocks.*

Symbol	Element	Weight Percent	Symbol	Element	Weight Percent
O	Oxygen	46.4	Pr	Praseodymium	0.00065
Si	Silicon	28.15	Dy	Dysprosium	0.00052
Al	Aluminum	8.23	Yb	Ytterbium	0.0003
Fe	Iron	5.63	Hf	Hafnium	0.0003
Ca	Calcium	4.15	Cs	Cesium	0.0003
Na	Sodium	2.36	Er	Erbium	0.00028
Mg	Magnesium	2.33	Be	Beryllium	0.00028
K	Potassium	2.09	U	Uranium	0.00027
Ti	Titanium	0.57	Br	Bromine	0.00025
H	Hydrogen	0.14	Ta	Tantalum	0.0002
P	Phosphorus	0.105	Sn	Tin	0.0002
Mn	Manganese	0.095	As	Arsenic	0.00018
F	Fluorine	0.0625	Ge	Germanium	0.00015
Ba	Barium	0.0425	W	Tungsten	0.00015
Sr	Strontium	0.0375	Mo	Molybdenum	0.00015
S	Sulphur	0.026	Ho	Holmium	0.00015
C	Carbon	0.020	Eu	Europium	0.00012
Zr	Zirconium	0.0165	Tb	Terbium	0.00011
V	Vanadium	0.0135	Lu	Lutetium	0.00008
Cl	Chlorine	0.013	I	Iodine	0.00005
Cr	Chromium	0.010	Tl	Thallium	0.000045
Rb	Rubidium	0.009	Tm	Thulium	0.000025
Ni	Nickel	0.0075	Sb	Antimony	0.00002
Zn	Zinc	0.0070	Cd	Cadmium	0.00002
Ce	Cerium	0.0067	Bi	Bismuth	0.000017
Cu	Copper	0.0055	In	Indium	0.00001
Y	Yttrium	0.0033	Hg	Mercury	0.000008
Nd	Neodymium	0.0028	Ag	Silver	0.000007
La	Lanthanum	0.0025	Se	Selenium	0.000005
Co	Cobalt	0.0025	A(r)	Argon	0.000004
Sc	Scandium	0.0022	Pd	Palladium	0.000001
N	Nitrogen	0.0020	Pt	Platinum	0.000001
Li	Lithium	0.0020	Te	Tellurium	0.000001
Nb	Niobium	0.0020	Ru	Ruthenium	0.000001
Ga	Gallium	0.0015	Rh	Rhodium	0.0000005
Pb	Lead	0.00125	Os	Osmium	0.0000005
B	Boron	0.0010	Au	Gold	0.0000004
Th	Thorium	0.00096	He	Helium	0.0000003
Sm	Samarium	0.00073	Re	Rhenium	0.0000001
Gd	Gadolinium	0.00073	Ir	Iridium	0.0000001

*A few very rare elements and short-lived radioactive elements are omitted.
SOURCE: After Brian Mason, 1966, and Konrad Krauskopf, 1968. Reprinted by permission from Brian Mason, *Principles of Geochemistry*, 3rd ed. (New York: John Wiley & Sons, 1966).

Periodic table of the elements

Light Metals | | Transitional Elements | | | Heavy Metals | | | | | | | Nonmetals

	IA	IIA	IIIB	IVB	VB	VIB	VIIB		VIIIB		IB	IIB	IIIA	IVA	VA	VIA	VIIA	VIIIA
1	1 **H** 1.0080																	2 **He** 4.003
2	3 **Li** 6.939	4 **Be** 9.012											5 **B** 10.81	6 **C** 12.011	7 **N** 14.007	8 **O** 15.9994	9 **F** 18.998	10 **Ne** 20.183
3	11 **Na** 22.990	12 **Mg** 24.31											13 **Al** 26.98	14 **Si** 28.09	15 **P** 30.974	16 **S** 32.064	17 **Cl** 35.453	18 **Ar** 39.948
4	19 **K** 39.102	20 **Ca** 40.08	21 **Sc** 44.96	22 **Ti** 47.90	23 **V** 50.94	24 **Cr** 52.00	25 **Mn** 54.94	26 **Fe** 55.85	27 **Co** 58.93	28 **Ni** 58.71	29 **Cu** 63.54	30 **Zn** 65.37	31 **Ga** 69.72	32 **Ge** 72.59	33 **As** 74.92	34 **Se** 78.96	35 **Br** 79.909	36 **Kr** 83.80
5	37 **Rb** 85.47	38 **Sr** 87.62	39 **Y** 88.91	40 **Zr** 91.22	41 **Nb** 92.91	42 **Mo** 95.94	43 **Tc** (99)	44 **Ru** 101.1	45 **Rh** 102.90	46 **Pd** 106.4	47 **Ag** 107.870	48 **Cd** 112.40	49 **In** 114.82	50 **Sn** 118.69	51 **Sb** 121.75	52 **Te** 127.60	53 **I** 126.90	54 **Xe** 131.30
6	55 **Cs** 132.91	56 **Ba** 137.34	57 TO 71	72 **Hf** 178.49	73 **Ta** 180.95	74 **W** 183.85	75 **Re** 186.2	76 **Os** 190.2	77 **Ir** 192.2	78 **Pt** 195.09	79 **Au** 197.0	80 **Hg** 200.59	81 **Tl** 204.37	82 **Pb** 207.19	83 **Bi** 208.98	84 **Po** (210)	85 **At** (210)	86 **Rn** (222)
7	87 **Fr** (223)	88 **Ra** 226.05	89 TO 103															

Rare Earth Elements

Lanthanide series

57 **La** 138.91	58 **Ce** 140.12	59 **Pr** 140.91	60 **Nd** 144.24	61 **Pm** (147)	62 **Sm** 150.35	63 **Eu** 151.96	64 **Gd** 157.25	65 **Tb** 158.92	66 **Dy** 162.50	67 **Ho** 164.93	68 **Er** 167.26	69 **Tm** 168.93	70 **Yb** 173.04	71 **Lu** 174.97

Actinide series

89 **Ac** (227)	90 **Th** 232.04	91 **Pa** (231)	92 **U** 238.03	93 **Np** (237)	94 **Pu** (242)	95 **Am** (243)	96 **Cm** (247)	97 **Bk** (249)	98 **Cf** (251)	99 **Es** (254)	100 **Fm** (253)	101 **Md** (256)	102 **No** (254)	103 **Lw** (257)

APPENDIX 2 Periodic table of the elements.

170

APPENDIX 3 Comparison of metric and English units.

UNITS		
1 kilometer (km)	=	1000 meters (m)
1 meter (m)	=	100 centimeters (cm)
1 centimeter (cm)	=	0.39 inches (in)
1 mile (mi)	=	5280 feet (ft)
1 foot (ft)	=	12 inches (in)
1 inch (in)	=	2.54 centimeters (cm)
1 square mile (mi^2)	=	640 acres (a)
1 kilogram (kg)	=	1000 grams (g)
1 pound (lb)	=	16 ounces (oz)
1 fathom	=	6 feet (ft)

CONVERSIONS		
When you want to convert:	Multiply by:	To find:
Length		
inches	2.54	centimeters
centimeters	0.39	inches
feet	0.30	meters
meters	3.28	feet
yards	0.91	meters
meters	1.09	yards
miles	1.61	kilometers
kilometers	0.62	miles
Area		
square inches	6.45	square centimeters
square centimeters	0.15	square inches
square feet	0.09	square meters
square meters	10.76	square feet
square miles	2.59	square kilometers
square kilometers	0.39	square miles
Volume		
cubic inches	16.38	cubic centimeters
cubic centimeters	0.06	cubic inches
cubic feet	0.028	cubic meters
cubic meters	35.3	cubic feet
cubic miles	4.17	cubic kilometers
cubic kilometers	0.24	cubic miles
liters	1.06	quarts
liters	0.26	gallons
cubic meters	264.2	gallons
gallons	3.78	liters
barrel (oil)	42.0	gallons

CONVERSIONS (continued)

When you want to convert:	Multiply by:	To find:
Masses and Weights		
ounces	20.33	grams
grams	0.035	ounces
pounds	0.45	kilograms
kilograms	2.205	pounds
metric tons	10^3	kilograms
long tons	2240.	pounds
short tons	2000.	pounds
metric tons	0.984	long tons
metric tons	1.102	short tons
Energy and Power		
joules	0.239	calories
calories	3.9685×10^{-3}	British thermal unit (BTU)
kilowatt hours	10^3	watt hours
kilowatt hours	3.6×10^6	joules
kilowatt hours	3413.	BTU
watts	3.4129	BTU per hour
watts	1.341×10^{-3}	horsepower
watts	1.	joule per second
watts	14.34	calories per minute

Temperature

When you want to convert degrees Fahrenheit (°F) to degrees Celsius (°C), subtract 32 degrees and divide by 1.8.

When you want to convert degrees Celsius (°C) to degrees Fahrenheit (°F), multiply by 1.8 and add 32 degrees.

When you want to convert degrees Celsius (°C) to kelvins (K), delete the degree symbol and add 273.

When you want to convert kelvins (K) to degrees Celsius (°C), add the degree symbol and subtract 273.

AVERAGE EQUIVALENTS

1 barrel oil weighs approximately 136.4 kilograms.
1 barrel oil is equivalent to approximately 0.22 metric ton coal.
1 barrel oil yields approximately 6.0×10^9 joules of energy.
1 metric ton of coal yields approximately 27.2×10^9 joules of energy.
1 barrel of cement weighs 170.5 kilograms.

APPENDIX 4 Rock classification.

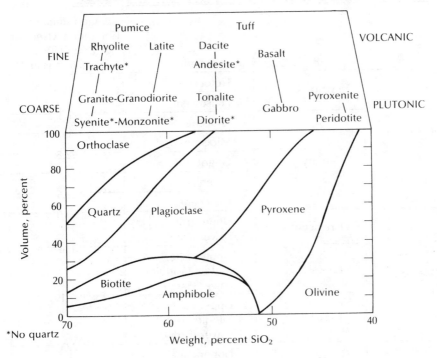

SOURCE: Oak Ridge National Laboratory, Report No. DWG 79–8325, 1979.

APPENDIX 5 Geologic time scale.

Era	Period	Series	Age Estimates Commonly Used for Boundaries (in million years)
Cenozoic	Quaternary	Holocene	
		Pleistocene	
	Tertiary	Pliocene	—1.8—
		Miocene	—5.0—
		Oligocene	—22.5—
		Eocene	—37.5—
		Paleocene	—53.5—
Mesozoic	Cretaceous	Upper (Late) Lower (Early)	—65.0—
	Jurassic	Upper (Late) Middle (Middle) Lower (Early)	—136—
	Triassic	Upper (Late) Middle (Middle) Lower (Early)	—190-195—
Paleozoic	Permian	Upper (Late) Lower (Early)	—225—
	Pennsylvanian	Upper (Late) Middle (Middle) Lower (Early)	—280—
	Mississippian	Upper (Late) Lower (Early)	—320—
	Devonian	Upper (Late) Middle (Middle) Lower (Early)	—345—
	Silurian	Upper (Late) Middle (Middle) Lower (Early)	—395—
	Ordovician	Upper (Late) Middle (Middle) Lower (Early)	—430-440—
	Cambrian	Upper (Late) Middle (Middle) Lower (Early)	—ca. 500—
			—570—

APPENDIX 5 (continued)

Time subdivisions of the Precambrian:

Precambrian Z—base of Cambrian to 800 m.y.*
Precambrian Y—800 m.y. to 1600 m.y.
Precambrian X—1600 m.y. to 2500 m.y.
Precambrian W—older than 2500 m.y.

---

*m.y. = million years

NOTE: Subdivisions in use by the U.S. Geological Survey.

APPENDIX 6   Important dates in the last 300 years.

1621	Coal-fired blast furnace used for iron smelting in England.
1627	First record of oil in the United States near the present town of Cuba, N. Y.
1629	The steam-jet turbine described.
1634–74	Coal discovered in northern Illinois.
1648	A gas-turbine device was demonstrated in England (a rotor driven by hot rising gases in a cylinder).
1743	The water turbine demonstrated.
1745	First blast furnace installed in England.
1747	Atmospheric electricity discovered by Benjamin Franklin.
1748	First coal mine opened near Richmond, Va.
1763	Anthracite discovered in the United States.
1769	Anthracite coal used in Pennsylvania forges.
1775	Natural gas discovered in the Ohio Valley.
1780	Iron-making established in all thirteen states.
	Native copper mined at Santa Rita, N. M.
1785	Charles de Coulomb formulated the law of electron charges (France).
1789	Electrolysis demonstrated in Holland.
1791	Principle of bimetallic batteries discovered by Luigi Galvani.
	Gas turbine patented in England by John Barber.
1800	Blast furnace operated by a steam engine.
	Alessandro Volta invented electric battery.
	Electroplating demonstrated in Germany.
1803	Steam locomotive built in England.
1804	First steam-driven electric locomotive operated in Wales.
1809	First steamboat operated between New York and Philadelphia in thirteen days.
1807	Sir Humphry Davy discovered sodium by electrolysis.
1813	First rock drill invented.
1816	Streets lighted with manufactured gas for the first time in the United States in Baltimore, Md.
1817	Coke used instead of charcoal for smelting at Plumsock, Pa.
1820	Electromagnet discovered by William Sturgeon of England, and Hans Christian Oersted of Denmark.
1821	Michael Faraday demonstrated electric motor in England.
	First natural-gas well drilled in Fredonia, N. Y.
1824	Basic principle of thermodynamics discovered by Sadi Carnot in France.

APPENDIX 6   (continued)

1830   Compressed air used for tunneling in England.

Steam hoist developed.

Reaper and steam-powered threshing machine invented by Cyrus McCormick. Mechanized agricultural age begins.

1831   First commercial steam turbine built by William Avery in the United States.

First electric generator built by Michael Faraday.

Electric dynamo invented in France.

1832   Water turbine invented in France.

1833   Michael Faraday suggested that current is carried in an electrolyte by ions.

Anthracite coal used in metal production in the United States.

1835   Coke used to produce good gray-forge iron.

1837   Electric motor patented in Vermont.

1839   First experimental electric locomotive operated between Washington and Bladensburg, Maryland.

1840   Because of discoveries by Galvani, Volta, Ampere, Ohm, Faraday, Franklin, Henry, and others, this is generally regarded as the beginning of the age of electricity.

1841   An improved method of drawing wire and spinning cables for bridges and hoisting invented by John A. Roebling.

1842   Coking coal discovered in Pennsylvania.

1843   Steam-shovel excavator operated in England.

Artificial fertilizers (superphosphates) sold in England.

1844   Artificial hydraulic cement manufactured.

1845   Blast furnace first used raw bituminous coal.

Iron ore discovered in Lake Superior district.

Upper Michigan copper production began. Production from this area totaled 129.3 million pounds by 1895.

1846–49 Gold discovered in the Black Hills of South Dakota but not revealed by discoverers.

1848   First oil refinery established in England.

California gold discovery.

Russian mining engineers discover gold on Kenai River, Alaska.

Iron ore smelted successfully in Lake Superior district.

1849   Microscope used to study physical metallurgy.

Compressed-air rock drill invented.

U.S. Department of Interior created.

1855   First practical computer built in Sweden.

APPENDIX 6   (continued)

1856	Development of synthetic coal-tar dyes.
	Aluminum produced electrolytically by Michael Faraday.
1857	Compressed-air rock drill developed in France.
1858	Discovery of Comstock Lode in Nevada.
1859	Oil discovered at Titusville, Pa. First oil well drilled.
1860	An expedition organized in San Francisco to prospect for gold in the Southwest. Gold discovered near Pinos Altos, N. M.
	First oil refinery built near Titusville, Pa.
	Synthetic rubber made.
	Internal-combustion engine commercially produced in Italy.
1860–70	Prospecting in the Southwest resulted in numerous mining operations and prospects in Arizona and New Mexico.
1860	Leadville, Colorado established.
1863	Natural gas used for industrial purposes in East Liverpool, Ohio.
	Motor car driven by an internal-combustion engine developed by Étienne Lenoir of Belgium.
1864	Lode claims for silver located at Butte, Montana. Output of gold and silver in the area valued at $1.2 million in 1878.
	Open-hearth furnace developed in France.
	Organization of St. Joseph Lead Co. to mine and smelt lead in Missouri.
	Gold-lead-silver mining started near Salt Lake City, Utah.
1865	Development of railroad tank car to transport crude oil.
	Formation of the first company to distribute natural gas at Fredonia, N. Y.
	First oil pipeline laid to transport oil 5 miles from Pithole City to Oil Creek Railroad, Pennsylvania.
1866	Atlantic cable installed.
1867	Invention of dynamite by Alfred Nobel.
1868	Copper shipped from Bingham Canyon, Utah.
	Gold production at Virginia City, Montana, totaled $30 million.
1869	Diamond drill brought from France to Bonne Terre, Mo.
1870s	Recognition of magnetohydrodynamic principle of generating electricity.
1871	Invention of rock drill by Ingersoll Rand.
1875–85	Pennsylvania Geological Society established first principles of modern petroleum engineering and geology.
1876	Homestake mine located in Black Hills, S. D. Organization of the Homestake Mining Co. the following year.
1877	Discovery of copper wealth near Bisbee, Arizona.

APPENDIX 6   (continued)

1879	Establishment of U.S. Geological Survey.
	Completion of first major oil pipeline 110 miles from Pithole City to Williamsport, Pa.
1879–83	Operation of numerous gold mining claims and prospects in Coeur d'Alene district of Idaho.
1880	Discovery of gold at Cripple Creek, Colorado, by Robert Womack.
	Tunnel bored with a pneumatic tunneler in England.
	Introduction of hydraulic rock drill.
1881	Organization of Anaconda Silver Mining Co. in Butte, Montana area.
1883	Confirmation of the anticlinal theory for accumulation of oil and gas by drilling.
1884	Multiple-stage steam turbine built in England by Sir Charles Parson.
1885	Development of petroleum cracking in the United States.
1886	Discovery of the electrometallurgical process of producing aluminum by Charles M. Hall (United States) and Paul Héroult (France) independently.
1887	Use of steel in pipelines.
1888	Production of manganese steel by Robert Hadfield.
1890s	Development of electrochemical process in the United States.
1891	Installation of first high-pressure long-distance pipeline to transport oil 120 miles from Greentown, Ind., to Chicago, Ill.
1894	Development of first oilfield near Santa Barbara, Calif.
	Export of kerosene to China by Standard Oil Co.
1895	Reorganization of the Anaconda Company to form the Anaconda Copper Mining Co.
1896	Discovery of radioactivity by Henri Becquerel of France.
1900	Marketed production of natural gas totaled 127 billion cubic feet. (Total was 24,700 billion cubic feet by 1975.)
1901	Use of solar energy to power a steam engine.
	Initiation of the first salt-dome production of oil near Beaumont, Texas.
	Motor oil marketed by Mobil Oil Co.
	Use of rotary drilling equipment at Spindletop oilfield in Texas.
1902	Operation of first satisfactory coal-face conveyor in the United States.
	England manufactured first all-metal car body of aluminum.
1903	Organization of Utah Copper Company. (Copper production started in 1907.)
	Installation of a 5,000- kilowatt steam turbine to generate electricity.

APPENDIX 6   (continued)

1904	Italian engineers drilled a steam well for operation of a small turbine.
	Operation of the first steam-powered tractor in California.
1905	Installation of first gasoline pump at Ft. Wayne, Ind.
1906–07	First aircraft manufactured in France and England.
1907	Household detergents manufactured in Germany.
1908	Discovery of oil in Middle East area (Iran).
1909	Installation in Oklahoma of first natural gas processing plant west of Mississippi River.
1910	Establishment of the Bureau of Mines, U.S. Department of Interior.
	Onshore drilling for oil in water in Louisiana.
1911	Flotation successfully used in the United States on zinc-lead ore at Butte, Montana.
1912	Demonstration of X-ray analysis of minerals.
1913	Patent of thermal cracking process to increase yield and quality of gasoline from petroleum.
1915	Start of low-cost high-tonnage gold mining at Juneau, Alaska.
1916	Manufacture of first nitrogen fertilizer in England.
1918	Discovery of nation's largest gas field in the Texas Panhandle.
1922	Use of geophysical instruments for oil exploration.
1923	Installation of mechanical coal-loading equipment to replace hand loading.
1925	Production of synthetic petroleum from coal in Europe.
1929	Use of electric logging equipment in oil wells.
1930	Production of wrought iron by continuous processes in Pennsylvania.
1930s	Development of the tungsten-carbide bit in Germany.
1930	Discovery of the largest U.S. oilfield in east Texas.
1932	Fission of the nucleus of the atom achieved by John Cockroft.
1937	Introduction of catalytic cracking in the U.S. petroleum industry.
1938	Commercial gasification of underground coal in Russia.
	Development of first offshore field in Louisiana.
1939	Demonstration of nuclear fission in Germany by Otto Hahn.
1942	Production of first man-made chain reaction at the University of Chicago by Enrico Fermi and coworkers.
	Preparation of the first pure compound of plutonium at the University of California.
1943	Successful treatment of taconite ore by E. W. Davis in Minnesota.
1945	Explosion of atomic bomb in the United States.

APPENDIX 6 (continued)

1947	Introduction of the modern scintillation counter to detect and measure radioactivity.
	Offshore well out of sight of land drilled off the Louisiana coast.
1949	Largest prospecting boom in the history of the United States triggered by the discovery of uranium ore at Haystack Butte, N. M.
1951	Manufacture of electronic computer.
1953	Gasification of underground coal in Alabama.
1954	The *Nautilus*, first nuclear powered submarine, was built at Groton, Mass. It traveled 69,138 miles on the first fueling.
	Establishment of the first atomic power station (5000 kilowatts) near Obninsk, Russia.
1956	Completion of first large-scale (90,000 kilowatts) atomic power station at Calder Hall, England.
1957	Commercial atomic power plant built at Shippingport, Pa.
1960	Power delivered by 12.5-megawatt geothermal steam plant in the United States. (Installed capacity for geothermal power was 600 megawatts by 1975.)
1963	Operation of a 60.9-megawatt liquid-metal fast-breeder reactor (LMFBR) in Michigan.
1967	Operations began at the Peach Bottom plant in Pennsylvania of a high-temperature gas-cooled reactor (HTGR).
1969	*Apollo XI* spacecraft landing of Neil Armstrong and Edwin Aldrin on the moon.
1970	Completion of a 275-mile pipeline to deliver coal from Black Mesa, Arizona, to the Mohave power plant at a cost of $35 million.
1970s	Operation of open-cycle magnetohydrodynamic powerplant with a considerable output by Soviet engineers.
1972	Launching of Landsat–1, formerly called ERTS–1, in the United States to transmit satellite imagery to the earth.
1973	Imposition of Arab Oil Embargo on the United States.
1974	Construction began on a 48-inch 800-mile pipeline from Prudhoe Bay to Valdez, Alaska.
	Opening of federal lands to development of geothermal power.
1975	Establishment of the Ocean Mining Administration by the United States.

SOURCE: U.S. Bureau of Mines, *Minerals Yearbook*, 1976.

Index

190

INDEX